Covered Bridges

OF THE SOUTH

Covered Bridges

OF THE
SOUTH

BY

RICHARD SANDERS ALLEN

BONANZA BOOKS · NEW YORK

ILLUSTRATION CREDITS

The author is grateful to the following people for their permission to use the illustrations in this book. The credits are given in the order in which the illustrations appear. Frontis from Elizabethton, Tenn., Chamber of Commerce. 1 & 2. Allen Collection. 3 & 4. North Carolina News Bureau. 5. Barbara Brainerd. 6 & 7. Eddy's Studio. 8. Barbara Brainerd. 9. Betty Gallup. 10. N.C. Dept. of Conservation & Development. 11. Barbara Brainerd. 12. N.C. Dept. of Conservation & Development. 13. N.C. News Bureau. 14. Betty Gallup. 15. N.C. Dept. of Conservation & Development. 16. *Forty Etchings* by Capt. Basil Hall, R.N. 1829. 17. Allen Collection. 18. Smithsonian Institution. 19 & 20. Sidney Pepe. 21. D. L. Sullivan. 22 & 23. Lucy G. Kemp. 24. Roy Brooks. 25. Smithsonian Institution. 26 & 27. Allen Collection. 28. Talmadge H. Veal. 29. Roy Brooks. 30 & 31. Lucy G. Kemp. 32. R. M. Harper. 33. Allen Collection. 34. Andrew Brown. 35. Sidney Pepe. 36. Allen Collection. 37 & 38. Andrew Brown. 39. Roy Brooks. 40–43. Roger Griffin. 44–46. Sam Breeden. 47. Smithsonian Institution. 48. Mrs. Hiram Gatchell Collection. 49. Sam Breeden. 50. Allen Collection. 51. Chaddock Collection. 52. Allen Collection. 53. Sidney Pepe. 54. Allen Collection. 55. Gene Bock. 56. Kentucky Dept. of Public Information. 57. Dr. George E. Gould. 58 & 59. Gene Bock. 60–62. Allen Collection. 63. Fred Kniffen. 64. Allen Collection. 65. Snider's Studio. 66 & 67. Texas Highway Dept.

O-517-128470
Copyright © MCMLXX by Richard Sanders Allen
Library Of Congress Catalog Card Number: 71-91311
All rights reserved.
This edition is published by Bonanza Books
a division of Crown Publishers, Inc.
by arrangement with The Stephen Greene Press.
a b c d e f g h
Manufactured in the United States Of America

ACKNOWLEDGMENTS

The research to complete this book was only made possible by a generous grant from the John Simon Guggenheim Memorial Foundation of New York, from whom the author received a 1962–63 Fellowship. I am in debt not only to the Foundation, but to those who had faith in my ability to carry out the project, and who said so.

A prime source of information was the archive material of various historical and engineering societies. This was obtained for the most part from personal perusal, with the aid of their fine and competent staffs. Among them were:

Alabama Historical Association, Birmingham
Arkansas History Commission, Little Rock
Baker Library, Harvard University, Boston
Engineering Societies Library, New York
Mississippi Department of Archives & History, Jackson
New York Historical Society, New York
New York Public Library, New York
New York State Library, Albany
North Carolina Department of Archives & History, Raleigh
Smithsonian Institution, Washington, D.C.
South Carolina Historical Society, Charleston
United States Patent Office, Washington, D.C.

A large number of state, county and local historical societies, highway departments, officials, civic groups and history-minded individuals contributed a wealth of material. Others unstintingly gave of their time and the results of their personal researches, among them:

ALABAMANS
Rucker Agee
R. M. Harper

GEORGIANS
Mrs. Kathryn Kennedy
Mrs. George W. Nelson
Harold L. Mills

KENTUCKIANS
Martin F. Schmidt
Mr. & Mrs. John E. Thierman

LOUISIANANS
Fred Kniffen
Ivan Nott

NORTH CAROLINANS
John Baskin
Dwight L. Crowell

Ted Davis
Michael J. Dunn
Betty Gallup
Mrs. Gettys Guille
Mrs. Lucille M. Johnson

SOUTH CAROLINANS
B. H. Eubanks
Richard S. Kirby
D. H. Sullivan

TENNESSEANS
Sam L. Breeden
A. F. Ganier
Charles Wilson
Ralph L. Winters

TEXAN
Tom H. Taylor

OTHERS
George W. Armstrong
Eugene R. Bock
Roy Brooks
John A. Diehl
Mr. & Mrs. Harold F. Eastman
Mrs. Herbert G. Foster
Mrs. Hiram R. Gatchell
Roger D. Griffin
Alvin W. Holmes
Mrs. Lucy G. Kemp
Mr. & Mrs. Orrin H. Lincoln
Leo Litwin
Sidney B. Pepe
Mr. & Mrs. John W. Poteet
William Schermerhorn
Miss Caroline Sprague
Raymond E. Wilson
Frederick C. Wunsch

SPECIAL APPRECIATION is also extended to Robert M. Vogel of The Smithsonian Institution, and to the late Dr. Albert B. Corey, Historian of the State of New York. R. S. A.

Doe River Bridge at Elizabethton, Tennessee.

CONTENTS

I   VINES ON THE EAVES   1

II   NORTH CAROLINA: The Proving of a Patent   3

III   SOUTH CAROLINA: Builders and Bunglers   9

IV   GEORGIA: The Well-kept and the Decrepit   15

V   ALABAMA: Not for Long the Longest   22

VI   TENNESSEE: A Few Volunteers   28

VII   KENTUCKY: Some Mountain Marvels   31

VIII   ALL GONE NOW   38

        MISSISSIPPI: Prisoners and Apathy   38

        ARKANSAS: A Hardy Specimen   42

        TEXAS: Sure We Did!   42

APPENDICES: I. WHAT MAKES A BRIDGE   44

           II. TABULATION OF EXISTING COVERED BRIDGES   46

GLOSSARY   49

SELECTED BIBLIOGRAPHY   51

INDEX   53

BUT WHY COVERED?   56

I

Vines on the Eaves

SOUTHERNERS have always been casual about their covered bridges. They built them where necessary, used them, and dispensed with them.

Some of the nation's longest and most unusual covered bridges were built in the South, embodying unique engineering features that were never tried elsewhere. They are deserving of far greater recognition than they have received.

The rate at which covered bridges are disappearing, especially in Alabama and Georgia, far exceeds the national average. As late as twenty years ago journalists wrote of the "last" covered bridges to be found in many rural areas, which in actuality still had dozens. But today it would be all too true.

Southern covered bridges invariably bring to mind a setting of flowers and lush vegetation. One old custom, now nearly forgotten, involved the weaving of a daisy chain across the entrance of a seldom-frequented piney woods bridge. Then began a nervous wait.

1. Former Hardeman's Mill Bridge at Nacoochie, Georgia.

"The first person to break it when they come through will be your new beau!"

A lady from Kentucky recalls spending the greater part of a summer's afternoon at this pastime, only to have the flowery links snapped and tangled by a rude boy on a bicycle.

"I was mad as hops then," she says, "but I've been married to him now for over fifty years."

"I did the same thing," says a grandmother with a soft southern accent, "and do you know who came along first? It was the meanest man in Blount County; with little red eyes and a billy-goat beard; riding a black mare as ugly as sin!"

Unfortunately, nostalgia has yet to save or keep in repair any southern covered bridges, and their once great numbers have dwindled to a sparse scattering across Dixie.

Due to the surveys of state highway departments and interested historical groups, the remaining covered bridges in the South can now be readily located, and in most cases easily reached by those who would seek them out.

Some of the glories of the Covered Bridges of the South are recorded in the state-by-state discussions that follow. Before it is fully too late, any partisans of the covered wooden bridge south of the Mason-Dixon line should keep in mind the words of Georgia's poet, Anderson M. Scruggs:

"Yet there are soulless men whose hand and brain
    Tear down what time will never give again."

2. The Buttahatchie River Bridge east of Aberdeen, Mississippi. Built originally to draw traffic to the town, it became known in its last years as "an old shanty bridge."

II
NORTH CAROLINA
The Proving of a Patent

IT WAS a Connecticut Yankee who introduced covered bridges to the Tarheel State. He was red-headed Ithiel Town of New Haven, a man well versed in architecture and heavy construction. After an apprenticeship with famed architect Asher Benjamin of Boston, Mr. Town acquired a solid reputation as the designer of two of New Haven's most prominent churches. Finding architectural fees hard to come by, the designer turned to the pressing need for adequate bridges up and down the seaboard of the loosely knit United States. Teaming with contractors who did the actual work, during 1816–18 Town successfully spanned the Connecticut River at three of its most important crossings.

In North Carolina lived wealthy Lewis Beard, son of one of the first settlers of Salisbury. His plantation fronted on the wide Yadkin River at a good site along the main thoroughfare to Winston-Salem. Beard kept a lucrative ferry, as did a competitive neighbor. After some years of altercation, the plantation owner petitioned the state legislature for the right to build a bridge. This granted, the next step was to find a reputable bridge architect. Beard engaged Ithiel Town.

On high piers above the often flooded waters of the Yadkin, some seven miles north of Salisbury, North Carolina's first covered bridge took shape during 1818. Ithiel Town must have received a handsome inducement to come down

3. Skeen Mill Bridge, built in 1901 over a branch of the Little Uwharrie River.

from Connecticut, and his "magnificent structure" is reported to have cost $30,000.

The following spring found the architect in
the town of Fayetteville, where he built another
toll structure called Clarendon Bridge. Recorded
as "a huge covered wooden bridge," this spanned
the Clarendon (now Cape Fear) River, and
served Fayetteville for forty-six years. It was ul-
timately burned by Confederate troops retreating before General William T. Sherman's advanc-
ing armies in March 1865.

Resourceful little Ithiel Town devised a bridge
truss of his own during his days in North Carolina. Making use of the pine planks available at
any sawmill, Town fashioned a lattice web of
timbers connected by wooden pins at the points
of intersection. He termed it his "Town lattice
mode" of bridge construction, and patented the
invention in 1820. Perhaps Town's Yadkin River
or Clarendon bridges were experimental proto-
types, fabricated in line with his original ideas
as to what constituted a good, sturdy, practical
bridge.

The architect spent most of the next decade in
the North, publicizing what turned out to be the
first important native American invention in
bridge trusses. Far more the astute promoter than
the actual contractor, Town journeyed up and
down the Atlantic seaboard in pursuit of both
architectural assignments and commitments to
build on his patent bridge plan. It was a rare
bridge project of any size whose backers did not
receive a visit from the gadabout Ithiel, and be
held immobile by his inspired oratory in favor of
the new "mode." For many companies formed
to build toll structures, he acted as consultant,
at least until the bridge building got well under
way. Despite the flamboyant approach of the
promoter, the Town-type bridge was a good design and worthy of every bit of acclaim and
trust it received.

At places which Ithiel Town was unable to
reach in his travels, duly appointed agents looked
after his interests. They collected a one-dollar-
per-foot royalty in advance of the building of a
Town lattice bridge, and double the amount if a
contractor was discovered who had been fool-
hardy enough to go ahead and build a patent
bridge without prepayment.

Among five state capitol buildings designed

4. Now by-passed, but intact, Skeen Mill is the
last of the town lattice bridges in the state in which
they were first built.

5. Near Moffit in Randolph County, North Carolina, was this span over Richland Creek, reached
by a typical open causeway.

6–7. *High Falls Bridge in Moore County was part of legacy of lattice truss construction left to North Carolina by Ithiel Town.*

8. *Red dirt roads led to onetime Spoon Bridge near Asheboro, N.C.*

in whole or in part by Ithiel Town was that of North Carolina at Raleigh. The job took seven years and called for frequent visits by the architect, who was doing other capitols for Ohio, Indiana and Illinois at the same time. Even with good fees from the state governments, Ithiel was not one to neglect his bread-and-butter interests, the patent bridges. During 1825 he took time to build a new lattice bridge over the South Yadkin River north of Salisbury, with Samuel Lemly as the actual contractor. Such was his fame by then that the crossing was long known as Ithiel Bridge. The spans doubtless served as a showcase for native builders to observe, and then to build their own of the same type.

Contractors in North Carolina were still erecting Town lattice bridges long after their inventor and his agents had passed from the scene. After Town's death in 1844, his designs came into the public domain and were a common feature of river crossings from the Carolinas on down into the Deep South as far as the northern counties of Mississippi.

Covered wooden bridges of both the lattice and less sophisticated types were once sprinkled across North Carolina from the coastal plains to the Blue Ridge. Back-country spans for the most part, they served through the seasons as dark passages for travelers over the tributaries of the Meherrin, the Neuse, Cape Fear River, the Yadkin, the Catawba and the French Broad.

Although Rutherford County in the western part of the state claims to have had more, it was dead-center Randolph which was always considered to be North Carolina's prime "covered bridge county."

Close to the heavily populated and industrialized Piedmont, Randolph was long a half-forgotten area of small farms and little crossroads settlements. Part of the county is occupied by the Uwharries, a geologically ancient range of low mountains seemingly dropped by chance on the level countryside. Watered by the Deep and the Uwharrie rivers, Randolph was once a pleasant area of rolling country roads, punctuated by little old mills and covered bridges at seemingly every sizable river and creek crossing. The county is reported to have had well over sixty covered bridges at one time, and as late as 1937 there were still forty-two.

Surprisingly, almost all of Randolph County's covered bridges were erected after 1900. Carpenter-contractor John C. Cox had much to do with making the region's total so high. He and his son, T. A. Cox, were responsible for building over twenty of the bridges. Operating from their farm home near Moffit's Mill south of Ramseur, the father-and-son team had the tools and know-how. They contracted directly with the county commissioners, who usually provided stone piers and abutments in advance, as bases from which the Coxes could throw a bridge across the stream. Before World War I they did very well financially, charging only $2.50 to $3.00 per foot if the timber was furnished, and $10.00 to $12.00 per foot if not. Sometimes the county even furnished convict labor, and in the case of a bridge at Brower's Mill, fifteen local volunteers did the whole job.

Without formal schooling, the Coxes simply used good sense to plan and erect either lattice or queenpost truss bridges at a variety of sites. As decoration they embellished some of their larger spans with the huge squared-off "storefront" portals so popular on small-town buildings of the era.

The younger Cox carried on until 1920. One of his bridges over Brush Creek, with two 50-foot spans, set a record for speedy erection. "T. A." superintended the job for Randolph County at $2.00 a day, and with four helpers had the bridge up in two weeks.

North Carolina's county road system was taken over by the state in 1931, and "progress" eventually came to out-of-the-way Randolph. The state's highway-improvement program accounts for the high rate of attrition of outmoded bridges. By 1947 there were only sixteen covered spans left in the county, and another decade reduced the total to two.

Two miles west of Pisgah, in a wooded valley between the slopes of the Uwharries, stands a bridge over a branch of Little River. With short buttresses, four to a side, it seems to span the stream on stepping stones, taking three spans to cover a total distance of only 54 feet.

To the northwest of Asheboro is Randolph County's other survivor—by-passed, blocked off, and lacking maintenance, but at least preserved for a while yet. This is Skeen Mill Bridge, built

9. *Flying buttresses and stepping stone piers distinguish surviving covered bridge 2 miles west of Pisgah, N.C.*

10. *Old time builder T. A. Cox demonstrates the boring machine with which he cut thousands of holes in the timbers of North Carolina's covered lattice bridges.*

11. *Former bridge over Brush Creek near Moffit in Randolph County.*

12. *Rolling Randolph County hills provide scenic setting for former covered bridge over Richland Creek.*

13. *Narrow confines, as in this former Randolph County span, led to speedy replacements by State of North Carolina.*

shortly after the turn of the century by Hezekiah Andrews, who learned his bridge-building from John C. Cox. It is the last of the Town lattice-truss bridges to stand in the state where the famous design was originally conceived.

To the west in Catawba County is North Carolina's only other existing covered bridge. Here the preservation picture is a bit brighter. The span, which crosses Lyles Creek east of Claremont, is known as the Bunker Hill Bridge. Eighty feet long, it was put up in 1895 by Andy L. Ramsour of Hickory with the help of Eli Kale, George Moller, Cain Bost and Rowell Electous Conner. Ramsour evidently had a good working knowledge of bridge construction, and utilized an old

14. *Preserved Bunker Hill Bridge east of Claremont in Catawba County, N.C. is one of only two remaining Haupt truss covered bridges in the U.S.*

BUNKER HILL BRIDGE

patent design that had been around for fifty years.

This was the special lattice design invented in 1839 by Pennsylvania engineer Herman Haupt. Haupt became famed as a tunnel builder and Civil War general, but his bridge plan was never very popular. It consisted of lattices in pairs slanting toward a center post. It was used here and there simply because it was described by the inventor in a book on bridge-building which enjoyed widespread sale for many years: Mr. Ramsour probably took his design directly from plans to be found in the popular Haupt book. Bunker Hill Bridge is important from an engineering standpoint as one of only two known examples of the type still in existence in the United States (the other stands in Thetford, Vermont).

As a result of joint efforts by the Catawba County Historical Association, the Newton Chamber of Commerce and the Claremont Lions Club, Bunker Hill Bridge has been kept in a reasonable state of repair. Today it is a feature of a small roadside park adjacent to combined U.S. Routes 64–70, and a mecca for admirers of North Carolina's nearly vanished covered bridges.

15. "Store front" portals surmount former Beane Mill Bridge near Ramseur, N.C.

III

SOUTH CAROLINA
Builders and Bunglers

ESPITE its small size and small total number of covered bridges on record—only about twenty—the Palmetto State was the scene of some noble experiments by eminent bridge builders, and is even involved in one of engineering's minor mysteries.

One of the earliest Carolina bridges of any consequence spanned the Congaree River at Granby, on the old road of Colonial days which became the main inland route across the state. A new crossing at this site (now Columbia), built in 1796, was of the usual trestlework fabrication of the period, but had the innovation of a clear 110-foot span over the main channel which must have involved some kind of truss-work. An "enterprising citizen," Colonel Wade Hamilton,

erected the bridge with a decided curve upstream, and took extraordinary pains to keep it secure against flood damage. It was 40 feet above normal water level with wood piers bolted into the solid rock bottom of the river, and further secured by having their footings based in boxes of melted lead. Despite these precautions, it was scarcely a dozen years before high water on the Congaree took Colonel Hamilton's bridge, and his hundred-year right of toll was made useless.

In the same year that the Congaree River Bridge was built, the well-known Philadelphia artist, Charles Willson Peale, devised the very first wooden bridge in America to receive a patent. Experimenting with model footbridges, Peale produced a plan for a soaring arch to span

BRIDGE ACROSS THE CONGAREE IN SOUTH CAROLINA

9

Drawn with the Camera Lucida by Captn B.Hall R.N.   Engraved by W.H.Lizars

16. English artist sketched long Congaree River Bridge at Columbia, S.C. while it was under construction in 1828.

the Schuylkill River. The painter-showman was convinced that the new nation needed bridges that would be both sturdy and cheap, and with spans long enough to preclude flood and ice damage.

Peale's bold scheme was to use laminated wooden arches of flat plank, keyed and wedged together, and utilizing unique bowed-truss paneling as a stiffening rail. Although the Pennsylvanian publicized his plans and ideas in a little booklet published in 1797, his own endeavors at bridge-building consisted of a quarter-scale model exhibited in his well-patronized museum.

It remained for Peale's itinerant painter-son Raphaelle actually to attempt building a real bridge on the patent plan. While on a wandering circuit of the South in 1805, the younger Peale contracted to build a full-scale laminated arch over a river "near Beaufort, S.C." This bridge was the first and only one on the Peale patent to be attempted. Perhaps the father's design exceeded his ne'er-do-well son's mechanical ability, or maybe the plan was a bit impractical to begin with. At any rate, the Beaufort attempt did not turn out well and it is not known whether the bridge was ever actually completed. Raphaelle Peale, always ready with an excuse, attributed

the failure to the fact that his workmen "were all Yankees," a sop to regional pride acceptable to South Carolinans.

Up the coast an open pile-and-trestle bridge was built in 1810 to span the Ashley River at the water-girt city of Charleston. This was a fine structure 30 feet wide and nearly a mile long, including the causeway. Its architect was one of those maligned Yankees: William Mills from Massachusetts.

17. Erection of Pee Dee River Bridge at Cheraw, S.C. is thought to have been supervised by truss inventor Ithiel Town. It stood for over a century.

Another builder-artisan from New England often traveled through the Carolinas in search of architectural assignments, and during his visits espoused the cause of his own radical patent bridge truss. Already acclaimed in North Carolina, Ithiel Town and his lattice mode of bridge construction were also quickly accepted farther south.

Early Town lattice spans, probably the first covered bridges in South Carolina, were built during 1823–29. Among them was a bridge mentioned only as "at Charleston," and the crossing of the Wateree River at Camden. A third example of this type took the main highway over the Pee Dee River at Cheraw. Patched and propped up by falsework, one span of the Pee Dee Bridge stood for over a century, serving U.S. Route 1 until the early 1930's.

Another early Carolina covered bridge eventually took the place of Colonel Wade Hamilton's

toll crossing at what became the capital city of Columbia. This was a substantial structure on the arch plan originally devised in 1805 by Theodore Burr of New York State; it stretched 1355 feet in 10 spans across the Congaree. The bridge had two carriageways and a $1 penalty sign admonishing users from proceeding on its boards at "faster than a walk."

Captain Basil Hall, an English naval captain who sketched the bridge while it was under construction in 1828, thought it extremely odd that Americans kept to the right-hand lane, in juxtaposition to English practice. He concluded his observations with the unflattering opinion that "it is not possible to conceive anything more ungraceful than these huge snail-like housings of bridges."

Both Columbia Bridge and the lattice crossing at Camden were destroyed during the scorched-earth campaign of William T. Sherman in 1865,

18. American version of controversial "Warren Truss" Bridge, as delineated by Russell Warren in 1852.

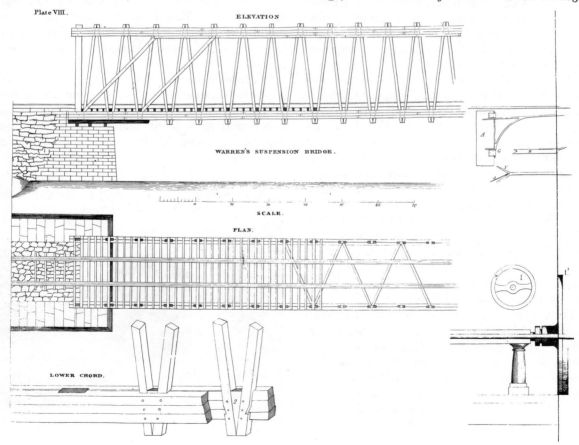

which finally brought war to the inland sections of the Carolinas.

Even in pre-Civil War days many Northerners lived in the South during the cold months. Among them was Russell Warren, a Rhode Island architect who was noted for his churches, banks, public buildings and private homes in the Providence area. Warren spent his winters in Charleston, where he also took on occasional architectural work.

A tradition in the Warren family is that Russell the architect "threw a bridge over the Great Pee Dee River, a feat that had been attempted by others who failed." Unhappily, the "tradition" tells no more of the bridge, its exact location or its subsequent history. As it is, Russell Warren continues to be part of an engineering historical enigma.

For years the term "Warren truss" has been loosely applied to bridges whose panel arrangement design in its simplest form resembles a series of letter W's between the chords. The truss has long been thought to be of English origin, stemming from an iron bridge patent granted in August 1848 to James Warren and Willoughby Theobald Monzani, both described as residents of the British Isles.

Not long after that date, Russell Warren of Providence, Rhode Island, U.S.A., furnished "Appleton's Mechanics Magazine" with a drawing of *his* wooden truss bridge, offered for railroad use, and on which he claimed patent rights. The published plate of the plan, appearing in an 1852 issue, seems generally to follow the "W" pattern of the Warren truss as it is known today.

Did Russell Warren copy James Warren's English iron design? As an established architect of considerable reputation, it seems highly unlikely. Perhaps it was simply a remarkable simultaneous design concept, arrived at on two continents independently, with the further coincidence of the same last name.

There is no true record of the American Warren's ever building a bridge, or holding a U.S. patent, which gives his English contemporary a better claim. Yet Russell certainly did devise a bridge truss and must have tried it out somewhere. Along the course of South Carolina's Pee Dee River some further information on the subject may someday come to light.

Most of South Carolina's covered bridges were built in the Piedmont region, where streams are fast flowing, with the potential power output of over half a million horses. Above the "fall line" rivers had steeper banks to give good footing for abutments, while in the lower half of the state, much of it not far above sea level, the causeway-pile-and-trestle construction was sufficient to bridge their meanderings.

The Graniteville Company, known as the South's oldest cotton-manufacturing organization, commenced operations in Aiken County back in 1845. Founder William Gregg built both his mill and the town of Graniteville in that year. Half a mile north, the company erected a covered bridge over Horse Creek to serve the road leading to Vaucluse. It was a little boxlike 43-foot span, horizontally sided and tightly shingled. Men and women on their way to and from work in the cotton mills crossed it for over a hundred years.

Almost as long-lived was Knox's Bridge, spanning the Tugaloo River at the Georgia state line to the west of Fair Play. This crossing was a private venture built under the direction of Colonel Samuel Knox, a landowner on the Georgia side.

For three months early in 1853, Colonel Knox's slaves felled trees along the Tugaloo above the bridge site, from which were prepared the hewn beams and sawn plank that would go into the proposed crossing. Downstream, granite blocks

19. Long tunnel of Knox Bridge, abandoned in its last years to vandals and the elements.

20. Built for lucrative tolls, Knox Bridge stretched over Tugaloo River to join South Carolina with Georgia.

were quarried, loaded on barges and poled up to the site. Knox used plans for a Town lattice structure, drawn up by Colonel Bowman of Elberton, Georgia. He employed a foreman on each bank of the river, and built out toward the middle. Completed in 1854, Knox's Bridge was 300 feet

21. Allen's Bridge once connected Laurens and Spartanburg Counties in South Carolina.

long in 3 spans, and cost the colonel $10,000.

It took the builder several years to realize a profit on the investment, but once paid for the bridge became a money maker. A doorlike barrier guarded either end, and the tolls were a flat 5 cents for foot passage, and 25 cents straight for vehicles. For half a century the estimated annual revenue was between two and three thousand dollars, a tidy sum for this rural region.

Barter in the form of chickens and farm produce often took the place of cash in payment for bridge tolls. One commodity that changed hands was a platform rocker, an antique chair which still graces the parlor of a Knox descendant. On the other hand there were the usual toll-evaders who tried and often succeeded in gaining free passage by means of a clamber up to the roof. Once two men paid a single nickel and went weaving across the long cool tunnel piggyback.

In 1908 Colonel Knox's heirs sold out to the adjoining states, and the bridge became free. Abandoned thirty years later with the advent of a new highway crossing downstream, Knox's Bridge withstood the elements, vandals and souvenir hunters until the 1950's.

Also shared with Georgia, one of South Carolina's three remaining covered bridges spans the Tugaloo River upstream from the Knox Bridge site, and serves the region between Westminster, South Carolina and Toccoa, Georgia. It is a two-span Town lattice called Prather's Bridge, and is one of only five interstate covered bridges still standing in the United States (the others are across the Connecticut River, joining New Hampshire with Vermont).

Elsewhere in South Carolina, the Long Cane Creek Bridge west of Troy in the Sumter National Forest is bypassed but standing. To the north, in the General Pickens Division of the same preserve, is found Chapman's Bridge over the Keowee River between Eastatoe and Jocassee.

Prather's and Chapman's are reminders of the days when most of South Carolina's covered bridges were dignified with names. There was Allen's Bridge, and Easley's, Lower Gassaway, Honea Path and Tumbling Shoals. Some were taken by flood, others drowned out by new reservoirs; but most succumbed to industrialized progress and the good roads system which has

22. *Joining South Carolina and Georgia, Prather's Bridge is one of only five interstate covered bridges in U.S.*

been extended throughout the state.

Harnessed by dams to provide vast power projects, the working rivers of the Piedmont still wend their winding way to the sea. But the covered bridges which once spanned them, with their ghosts of Ithiel Town, Russell Warren and Colonel Knox are all but gone.

23. *A vista of wintry Georgia countryside from interstate Prather's Bridge.*

IV

GEORGIA
The Well-kept and the Decrepit

UNTIL recent years no real tabulation of covered bridges in Georgia had ever been made. A couple of dozen were on the state highway system, to be replaced one by one as funds permitted. As for the vast network of county roads, well, it was anybody's guess.

Determined researchers like Harold Mills of Millen and Howard MacKenzie of Toledo, Ohio, queried each of the Peach State's 159 counties, meeting with mixed reactions and conclusions. County officials reported vaguely "one or two in the western part," or confused things by listing covered bridges on county lines as completely under their jurisdiction, while road commissioners of adjoining counties did the same.

The Georgia State Highway Department finally made a concentrated effort at listing in 1955, and came up with a total of seventy-seven, including two on the South Carolina state line. Personal visits by bridge buffs such as Mills, MacKenzie, George Armstrong, Fred Wunsch and Roger Griffin have served as a doublecheck on the state's listing, and what were once obscure "locations" are now tangible sites of covered bridges.

Floods, fires, vandalism and progress have drastically reduced the ranks of covered bridges in Georgia during the past decade. The total now stands between 20 and 30, scattered over some twenty counties. There are records of at least 185 timbered tunnels that once stood in the state, and the all-time total is probably a conservative 250.

Local notice of Georgia covered bridges in pre-Civil War days is fragmentary, but what has been preserved shows that then, as in later years, the preference for this type of structure was naturally strong in the wooded northern section of the state.

By far the most popular type of construction was the Town lattice, doubtless introduced as a result of the successful examples built and promoted by inventor Ithiel Town in the neighboring Carolinas. The first known Georgia bridge of that type spanned the Chattahoochee River on the Alabama line at Columbus in 1832. Virtually any sizable covered bridge in North Georgia was (and still is) on the Town mode of construction. County commissioners even took to specifying "a lattice bridge" in advertising for bids from contractors. The type was popular with succeeding generations of builders, and they were replaced in kind. One substantial Town plan bridge was built over the Hudson River in

24. Pumpkin Creek Bridge in Paulding County, Georgia included long open approach. Guardrails were considered an extravagance.

25. *Famed Glass Bridge over the Chattahoochee River near La Grange was for long Georgia's longest.*

26. *Ante-bellum covered bridges served Georgia cities of Augusta (above), and Columbia. Horace King built latter.*

Banks County as late as 1915.

Stemming from railroad practice, a few wood and iron Howe truss bridges were erected in Georgia during the latter part of the nineteenth century, but they never seriously challenged the traditional preference for the Town lattice type. For very small streams, local builders used simple framed structures on the kingpost and queenpost plans, sometimes substituting iron rods for the wooden uprights. As elsewhere in the South, swampy river bottoms in many cases necessitated long open trestle approaches, with the covered portion erected only to span the main river channel.

Covered-bridge builders in Georgia were in general a modest lot, and only a few of their names have been recorded. Among them are men like J. W. Baughman of Early County, Herman Williams of Banks, W. T. Bryant of Bellevue (near Talbotton) and Ben Smith of Dahlonega.

Georgia's best-known covered-bridge builder was Horace King of LaGrange, the man who erected the state's first known weatherboarded and roofed crossing at Columbus. King, of mixed Negro, Indian and Caucasian lineage, was born in South Carolina in 1807. As a young slave he showed great aptitude toward carpentry and heavy construction, and is reported to have built "at least one covered bridge over the Pee Dee River" in his native state.

At the age of twenty-three the slave was acquired by a Carolina house builder and contractor, John Godwin, who recognized the young man's capabilities and sent him North to be properly educated. In 1832 Horace and his master moved to Girard (now Phenix City), Alabama, just across the Chattahoochee from Columbus, Georgia. Godwin secured contracts and his talented slave was soon busily engaged in erecting a long, two-span bridge to connect the adjoining towns. The first Town lattice to be built in the region, the interstate crossing was a showpiece for both the type and its builders. It launched Horace King on a bridge-contracting career that was to cover forty years.

An enlightened master, John Godwin freed King in 1848. For a Negro, even a freedman, to be building the best of bridges was an unusual situation in the Deep South. King's white friends in Georgia and Alabama pushed through identical bills in the legislatures of both states, permitting the ex-slave to conduct business on a fair and equal footing with other contractors.

Operating out of LaGrange, Georgia from 1850 on, Horace King was the man to whom authorities turned when a bridge was needed. He supervised construction of at least a dozen highway and railroad bridges over the Chattahoochee, the famous Georgia river that brings red soil down from the Habersham County hills on its way to the Gulf of Mexico.

In 1858, referred to simply as "Horace, the bridge builder," he contracted to span the Flint River at Albany. Up at Milledgeville, King had already prepared timber for a crossing of the Oconee, and it was stacked at the bridge site. Due to some unknown difficulty or delay, construction at Albany was more urgent than at the Baldwin County seat. The resourceful contractor loaded his cut and seasoned chords and lattices aboard some railroad flatcars and shipped them south. The bridge prepared for Milledgeville became Albany's crossing of the Flint. Though the practice had commenced with railroad bridges, this is one of the first recorded instances of prefabricated timbers for a highway bridge being shipped to the site by train.

During Reconstruction days, Horace King was very active rebuilding Georgia's war-wrecked bridges. A new crossing replaced his old work at Columbus, which had been put to the torch by Union troops in 1865. To accommodate the mills and manufactories upstream he soon constructed a second structure to span the Chattahoochee. Down at Fort Gaines, the foundations for an interstate bridge caught the brunt of an August freshet in 1868. A cofferdam and center pier disappeared under the red water, along with thirteen workmen. When the contractors quit, it was Horace King who was called in to successfully complete the job. Since he passed the arts of bridge-building on to his four sons, it was one of them, William, who repaired the Fort Gaines crossing after damage in 1888, and a grandson replaced two spans after the great flood of 1913.

King never forgot the man who made his success possible. In Phenix City's old Girard Cemetery is the only known monument erected by a slave to his former master. On John Godwin's

tomb is an iron slab inscribed: "In lasting re-
membrance of his love and gratitude for his lost
friend."

Amid the mists of Georgia folklore is mention
of another ex-slave contractor. He was given as
a boy to a Presbyterian minister from Connecticut named Pratt, from whom he took his name,
and who freed and educated him as a mechanic.
Later, during Reconstruction times, Pratt built
covered bridges in the Atlanta area, and in
northeastern Georgia.

Common to Georgia and other southern states
was the covered wooden railroad bridge. These
were built in great profusion throughout the
region; they were usually heavier versions of
the Town and Howe patent plans.

When Civil War came to the South, communi-
cations became all-important, and covered
wooden bridges were extremely vulnerable links
in the railway network. At important crossings
they were stripped of their fire-prone roof and
siding. Armed guards, quartered in wooden
blockhouses at either end, would patrol stra-
tegically-located bridges, and nobody got across
without a pass. Sometimes the bridges were left
enclosed and fitted with thick doors at either
end. At isolated sites where guerrilla raids were
frequent, they served small defending garrisons
as passable forts.

In Georgia, one of the war's most colorful
exploits was the so-called Andrews Raid involv-
ing the famous locomotive "General." Even previous to the recent centennial of the event, this
story had been recounted in magazines, books,
TV programs and at least two motion pictures,
including a bang-up Walt Disney version. In the
spate of telling and retelling, many details of the
"great locomotive chase" have become distorted,
with the episode rapidly attaining the status of
folk legend.

Actually, the 1862 "Chattanooga Railroad Expedition" of secret agent James J. Andrews and
his Ohio volunteers contained enough daring
and spectacular melodrama to go down in history without a bit of embellishment. What is
usually forgotten is the reason for the famous
raid, which was not merely to steal a train and
go steaming through the Georgia hills blasting
away at Johnny Rebs.

The Expedition's main and avowed purpose
was to burn the covered wooden bridges along
the line of the Western & Atlantic Railroad in
Georgia and Tennessee. These included the two
lengthy structures over the Etowah and Oosten-

27. *Gen. Sherman's march to the sea included the burning of Georgia bridges such as the one depicted
in old drawing.*

28. *Long Bridge near Waycross, Georgia was built to span possible floodwater width of normally small, sluggish stream.*

aula rivers, and eleven smaller spans over Chickamauga Creek. Such a coup would destroy the Confederate supply line and open the way for Union capture of the city of Chattanooga.

Unfortunately for Andrews and his nineteen men (two more overslept and did not make the party), both the bridges and the firewood with which to burn them were thoroughly soaked in the April rains. Their train, stolen at Big Shanty, Georgia and pulled by the "General," could never get far enough ahead of the pursuing Confederates to stop and properly set a bridge afire. After an 80-mile chase, beyond Dalton, the raiders decided on a last desperate try.

Just ahead stretched a long bridge over the Chickamauga, the burning of which might mean the difference between the raid's success or failure. Behind, the smoke of a pursuing Confederate engine could be clearly seen. Andrews and his men in the "General" brought back hot embers from the locomotive to start a blaze on the floor of their last boxcar. Smoldering fitfully, the coals took hold. Cheering with renewed hope, the raiders took refuge in the near-empty tender as the "General" rumbled into the bridge. The blazing car was uncoupled in the middle of the long dim tunnel, and the incendiaries pulled out of the smoky darkness. A little way beyond they stopped to watch results.

The "Texas," which had been commandeered by Conductor William A. Fuller of the stolen train, soon steamed into view. Flames in the

bridge glowed red, but Fuller's engine only slowed and then resolutely plunged on. The Andrews men in the "General" were stunned as the blazing boxcar popped out of the bridge on their side, pushed clear by the "Texas." Fuller and his Southerners, eyes stinging with smoke and hot sparks scorching their clothes, shoved the car to a nearby siding and resumed the chase.

This last blow was too much for the Union bridge burners, who had dared and risked so much only to meet failure because of bad weather. The ungreased "General," her fire box empty, clanked to a stop a few miles farther north. The men took to the piney woods but all were captured. James J. Andrews and seven members of the party were hanged as spies. The rest either escaped from Southern prisons or were eventually exchanged. The survivors were the first American soldiers to receive the newly-established Congressional Medal of Honor.

Charred but serviceable, the covered bridges which the raiders had hoped to destroy stood stanch until another Northern invader marched into Georgia two years later. Close on the heels of General William T. Sherman's troops came General Daniel McCallum's Railway Construction Corps. Working incredibly fast, they repaired the right of way and slapped up new bridges almost as speedily as the retreating Confederates had burned the old ones. By war's end in 1865, a Federal force which sometimes numbered as many as ten thousand men had built or rebuilt twenty-six miles of wooden railroad bridges.

Today Little Banks County, with a one-time

29. *A long Howe truss bridge south of West Point, Georgia, stripped of its weatherboarding in preparation for replacement.*

30. *Typical rural Georgia bridge in Banks County. This spans Hickory Level Creek north of Maysville.*

high of thirty covered bridges once standing within its borders, still leads the State of Georgia with five remaining spans. It is the center of a cluster of existing covered bridges in the hilly northeast section of the state. For the most part tucked away on byroads, the bridges in this section range in size from the tiny 33-foot Chickamauga Creek Bridge in White County to Georgia's longest, a 4-span 236-foot lattice crossing of Broad River near Carlton between Madison and Oglethorpe counties. Perched on high piers, and reached by open approach spans, the bridges of this area stretch from bank to bank of streams with such picturesque names as Amicalola, Hickory Level and Big Clouds. Tops when it comes to unique nomenclature is the Poole Mill Bridge between Ducktown and Frogtown over Sittingdown Creek.

To the northwest of the state capital of Atlanta two more covered bridges appear to have a good chance for continued survival. Local interest is high in the eighty-year-old structure on huge piers at Euharlee, and in one over Sope's Creek, close by a residential district near Smyrna.

Located near the Alabama line ten miles north of West Point was the famous Glass Bridge, first erected in 1870 by a builder from Athens named McCollom. It burned before completion and three years later Horace King of La Grange threw one of his monster Town lattice fabrications across its scorched stone piers. In six spans, it stretched 614 feet across the Chattahoochee. Always called Glass Bridge for a nearby family, the crossing appears to have been under repair

or replacement in August, 1896, when it again caught fire and was destroyed. Gainesville contractor James Nunn immediately rebuilt it, and his bridge designer, W. H. Armstrong, came up with plans for a duplicate of Horace King's old lattice bridge. It was fitting that during the erection Horace's sons John and Horace were in charge of the carpentry and labor gangs.

The last covered Glass Bridge stood for nearly sixty years, a long dark tunnel of criss-crossed plank which afforded Georgia-Alabama farm people their only crossing of the Chattahoochee in twenty miles. Far from the quick peck possible in a short "kissing bridge," the length of Glass Bridge provided time for a lengthy romance.

Mrs. Mary Glass recalled the inky interior as she and her husband occasionally had to return home after dark. "Mary," he told her once, "Don't care what you say, just keep talking to me, and hope the hoss ain't lost!"

In the late 1940's and '50's, despite remonstrances by local people and historical groups, Glass Bridge was allowed to deteriorate until it would have been condemned on its appearance alone. The rickety ruin was replaced by the state in 1955.

Today's five remaining covered bridges in the LaGrange-Thomaston area of western Georgia are only puny reminders of the bridge-building legacy left by Horace King. Had efforts to save Glass Bridge been successful, the region would today be a tourist mecca, boasting the longest covered wooden bridge in the United States.

31. *College Avenue Bridge in Athens, well-known to generations of University of Georgia students, now graces Stone Mountain Memorial Park.*

More satisfactory results were reached at Athens, where a drive to preserve the old College Avenue Bridge over the North Fork of the Oconee met with success. Well-trodden by generations of University of Georgia students, the 162-foot Town lattice span has been moved and re-erected in Stone Mountain Memorial Park. And at famed Callaway Gardens a portion of a former covered bridge from Troup County was placed over a ditch on the grounds for use as a footbridge.

Far downstate in Early County are more signs of the recognition of the historical worth of saving some of the old Georgia bridges before time removes them forever. In 1957 the Peter Early Chapter, Daughters of the American Revolution, adopted a program of protection for the last two covered bridges still standing in the county. Sparked by Mrs. George W. Nelson, who appeared before the County Board of Commissioners to appeal for preservation, the D.A.R. ladies were made custodians of the bridges, and they now take it on themselves to report any needed repairs to the superintendent of roads. The Peter Early Chapter has also instigated a beautification program for the areas immediately surrounding the bridges, and much favorable publicity has been directed to the county as a last stronghold of the timbered tunnel.

32. Coheelee Creek Bridge in Early County, Georgia is the next-to-southernmost covered bridge in the United States.

Located southwest of Blakely, the bridges stand amid tangled wild gardens of mountain laurel, sumac, callicarpa, honeysuckle and hydrangea. Bronze directional signs supplied by the Georgia Historical Commission direct visitors to the Coheelee Creek bridge on the river road north of Hilton, and to that over Sowhatchee Creek on the other side of Route 62. This last bridge has a singular distinction. It is the southernmost covered bridge on a public highway in the United States.

V
ALABAMA
Not for Long the Longest

ONCE there was an abundance of covered bridges in Alabama. The majority were built over the eroded streambeds of the great Stone Mountain Plateau at the lower end of the Appalachian Mountain chain. From Sand Mountain, some of the creeks drain north into the Tennessee River, while others form tributaries of the Alabama and Black Warrior rivers to the southwest, and the Chattahoochee, which adjoins part of the Georgia border.

With well-timbered terrain, and an annual rainfall of 55 inches flowing off through deep valleys, northern Alabama was a logical place to build covered bridges. Early roads followed old Indian trails and crossed at natural shallow fords. With the advent of bridges, the crossings became bolder and more direct, accounting for the numerous high and long covered structures which for years were ignored as "just bridges" by unhurried citizens of the state.

Much of Alabama's covered-bridge history parallels that of neighboring Georgia. The majority of structures followed the lattice plan of Ithiel Town, introduced in the 1820's. In a promotional treatise on building his patent bridges, Mr. Town noted the existence of a crossing erected on his mode in Alabama. It was erected around 1830 over the Black Warrior River at Tuscaloosa.

Then too, freedman-bridge builder Horace King was once a resident of Phenix City. His fine bridges on the Town plan which crossed

33. One of Alabama's longer covered bridges spanned Warrior River south of Arab.

the Chattahoochee aroused admiration, and like the Tuscaloosa Bridge influenced builders to try this type elsewhere in Alabama.

Tradition dies hard in the Deep South, and succeeding generations of bridge contractors resisted the substitution of any other truss form. They stuck to Town's lattice plan for over eighty years, and their confidence and trust were not misplaced.

Occasionally the later years saw a Howe patent bridge or two erected near the more enlightened urban areas. And at isolated crossings where a short span would suffice, a few simple trusses were attempted.

One native professional bridge builder who bucked the prevailing preference for latticework was Lowndes County's John R. Remington. Though he built conventional wooden bridges for both highways and railroads, Remington also dabbled in cotton-press and steam-mill improvements. An inveterate experimenter, he even patented a special coffee pot.

During a sojourn in England in 1847, Mr. Remington devised a curious wooden bridge, and built the prototype over the River Trent at Shirleywich in Staffordshire. This "novelty in bridge building" was a thin, inverted arch with glued joints. Combining suspension and cantilever principles, together with some unheard-of theories on the tensile strength of wood, it was followed by two additional spans, erected at British amusement parks. Despite its actual existence, the debut of the "Remington bridge" was greeted with disbelief and derision by the engineering profession.

Returning to America, John Remington attempted to capitalize on his invention, which he had already patented in 1843. He published a descriptive pamphlet about it, and exhibited a model of the unusual structure in both New York and New Orleans. Visitors to his offices were invited to run and jump upon the model, which withstood all efforts to break it down. Spectators reported that "the fragile-looking thing" had an uncanny resilience, which seems to prove that Remington's theories on the strength of wood fibers and his application of them must have contained much of merit.

Back in Alabama in 1850, the inventor received permission from the Montgomery City Council

34. *Former hooded crossing of Pintlala Creek between Montgomery and Lowndes counties, Alabama.*

to erect one of his patent bridges over a ravine at the foot of Coosa Street, between the city and the Alabama River wharf. The structure was to be built at Remington's own expense.

Though obviously put up to endeavor to prove the worth of his construction principles, John Remington's suspension bridge at Montgomery was stupendous. It was not graced with any weather protection, or even hand rails, but at 436 feet it was the longest single-span wooden bridge ever built in the world. Only about 10 feet wide, its open deck stretched in a swooping arc at a dizzy height above the deep gully, connecting the city's depot with the road to the ferry.

Calvin Sayre, a young Montgomery sport, saddled up and rode the first horse across the bridge. Emboldened, he then drove carefully back across the yawning gulf with his steed hitched to a buggy.

It would be pleasant to record that John Remington and his world-record bridge found instant fame and acclaim. Actually, after reaching the pinnacle of the Montgomery grand opening, absolutely nothing more appears to have been written about either. It is of course extremely doubtful that an unprotected, glued-together suspension bridge of wood would manage to hold together for any length of time. Its almost inevitable tumble to destruction probably took along John Remington's dreams of recognition as a bridge-truss inventor.

Though not related to Remington's venture, for

35. *Alabama's Horseshoe Bend Bridge across the Tallapoosa River was for eight years the nation's longest.*

eight years Alabama could claim the nation's longest wooden bridge. This was the crossing of the Tallapoosa River at Horseshoe Bend, a site made famous as the battleground where Andrew Jackson's citizen-soldiers broke the power of the Creek Indians on March 27, 1814. Two other well-known historical figures, Davy Crockett and Sam Houston, also took part in this battle.

Possibly there was a previous covered bridge at Horseshoe Bend, but the last one there was

37. *Erected on concrete caissons, a long Town lattice bridge spanned Bear Creek near Margerum in Colbert County, Alabama.*

36. *Old buttressed covered bridge spanned De Soto River near Mentone, Alabama.*

built long after such structures were ordinarily erected. Joe Winn of Dadeville took the contract to build it in 1907–08, for which Tallapoosa County paid him $13,986.00.

Mr. Winn's contribution to superlatives in bridge lengths was a narrow Town lattice structure mounted on five masonry piers. He did not connect his plank with iron bolts, as had

38. *For this photo and the one below see 37.*

by that time become the fashion, but joined them with some 1600 white-oak pegs, or "trunnels." Another old-time touch was to tightly weatherboard the bridge with horizontal siding.

Complete, the four spans of 150 feet each stretched a full 600 feet across the Tallapoosa. The footage figure of five additional approach spans, built with low iron trusses, was often listed, giving the impression of even greater length.

With flood destruction in 1955 of a covered bridge across the Delaware River between Pennsylvania and New Jersey, the long Alabama specimen assumed top honors for the United States. It was soon bypassed by a new state highway bridge but allowed to remain as a pedestrian crossing and curiosity for visitors.

Organized effort in 1956 led to the designation of Horseshoe Bend as a National Military Park. Though the National Park Service had planned to preserve the bridge, acquisition by the government, and money available under "Mission 66" projects came late. Braced and patched, with broken chords and blue sky showing through the roof in hundreds of places, the old bridge waited for restoration. One night in July, 1963, one tired span collapsed and the chain reaction brought down the others. Now the nation's longest covered bridge is in New England. (Windsor, Vt.–Cornish, N.H.)

Apathy and neglect, which doomed Alabama's greatest claim to covered-bridge fame, unfortunately still are widespread in the Cotton State. From a total of well over fifty a dozen years back, 'Bama's covered spans now number less than twenty. Of these, over a third are abandoned, left to rot and eventually leave the scene with the crash, splash and splintering of once sound timbers.

The counties of the Sand Mountain Plateau, once rich in covered bridges, can still claim a few pitiful remainders, including some surpris-

39. *With maintenance like this, it is little wonder that deep south covered bridges were short-lived. Near Burkeville, Ala.*

40. *Pintlala Creek Bridge on Lowndes-Moody county line sported flat roof reminiscent of Iowa covered bridges. It collapsed in 1965.*

ingly long and high spans. Two crossings of Locust Fork in Blount County are over 300 feet in length; that near Nectar stretches 371 feet in four spans. Also in Blount County is Horton's Mills Bridge, founded on natural rock abutments some seventy feet above Calvert Prong.

Calhoun County is today reduced to three short spans: the Mellon Bridge over Choccolocco Creek, one at Coldwater, and an abandoned structure over Tallahatchee Creek. Also abandoned is Cullman County's lone survivor, near Clarkson, a long lattice high above Crooked Creek.

At Keener in Etowah County stands a ramshackle oddity in covered bridges. With a main span built of steel truss columns, and wooden rafters under an iron roof, this crossing is reached by a pair of inclined approach spans, also of iron framework and similarly topped. Plank weatherboarding on this metal skeleton was long ago replaced with galvanized iron sheets, most of which have also now disappeared. When the bridge was bypassed in recent years, a local garden club planned to retain this monstrosity, but the latest word is that such a course has proved to be "economically unfeasible." Five miles down the valley was the equally abandoned Reece City (or Reeceville) Bridge, mercifully out of sight of U.S. Route 11. Canting like a tipsy dowager, this bridge was temporarily kept out of the waters of Little Wills Creek only by the unusually heavy diagonal outside plank-

ing which supplements the original lattice truss. It has recently been moved to Noccalula Falls near Gadsden, a commendable undertaking.

To the west of the Talladega National Forest, the Kymulga and Riddle's Mills bridges still span Talladega Creek, while in Coosa County is a little country bridge southwest of Alexander City in the Thomas Store neighborhood.

North of Phenix City, in the region where Horace King's bridges once were famed, there are two more recent examples of the old lattice plan still spanning back-country creeks in Lee County.

Even a bridge with memories of "The War" stands disused in Sumter County. Back in 1861 a new bridge was badly needed to span Sucarnoochee River at Livingston. It was important enough for Captain W. A. C. Jones, C.S.A. to take time out from the hostilities to build. In 1924, Jones' well-constructed bridge was moved some twelve miles as the crow flies, and re-erected over Alamuchee Creek near Bellamy. There it stood until bypassed in recent years.

Surveying the general condition of decay and short life expectancy for most of Alabama's covered bridges, the only other recent bright spot seems to be in the extreme northwestern corner of the state. Southwest of Cherokee stands a 94-foot Town lattice bridge over Buzzard Roost Creek. Though it bears a sign proclaiming "built in 1820," the actual erection date is doubtless

41. *Typical of Alabama spans which stood until recent years was Sougchatchee Creek Bridge.*

42. *Captain Jones took leave from the Confederate Army to build this bridge in 1861. Later moved, it stands near Bellamy, Ala.*

several decades later. In 1952 it was thought worthwhile to restore the span; the Cherokee Lions Club sponsored a refurbishing and re-painting job carried out by the Colbert County Board of Revenue. The bridge was recently re-turned to its site, after near-loss in a flash flood.

Now Buzzard's Roost Bridge has been acquired by the Federal Government's nearby Natchez Trace Parkway. Preservation and public use will be under the jurisdiction of the National Park Service. Perhaps the opportunities lost at Horse-shoe Bend may yet be realized here, and at least one covered bridge in Alabama assured of a de-gree of permanence.

43. *Buzzard's Roost Bridge in Colbert County was saved from a flood; is now park of National Park Service's parkway restoration of Natchez Trace.*

VI
TENNESSEE
A Few Volunteers

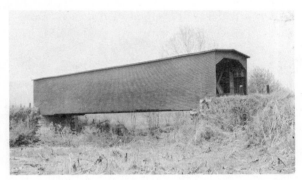

44. Neatly-sided Brice Bridge northeast of Knoxville is oldest in state of Tennessee.

45 & 46. Tennessee's best-known covered span, the city-owned Doe River Bridge at Elizabethton. 1000 cars still cross it daily.

BUILT in the years immediately after the Civil War, most of the remaining covered bridges in Tennessee are approaching the century mark. Oldest in the state is Brice's Bridge, a tightly boxed-in crossing of Big Flat Creek on the old Rutledge Pike to the northeast of Knoxville. Built in 1876, on the Howe plan common to the state's large bridges, Brice's has a roof with little pitch and no overhang. It compensates for protection from the elements by sporting unusual sheathed sides which are clapboarded from top to bottom.

Horizontal siding is also a feature of Tennessee's best known covered bridge, the city-owned span over the Doe River at Elizabethton. Built in 1885 in what was then the main business district of town, it is singular in appearance for an American covered bridge, resembling greatly those of Switzerland, Bavaria and New Brunswick, Canada. At each end great diagonal shelter panels protrude, and a sloping triangular roof comes down from the ridgepole to top them.

Elizabethton's covered bridge survived the "Big Tide" of May 1901, when a cloudburst of unprecedented proportions raised the levels of the Watauga and Doe rivers. In addition to the flood of water, great booms of logs from mountain lumber operations came riding the crest, each a battering projectile. Steel and iron rail and highway bridges in the valleys were carried away by the "Big Tide," and hundreds of spectators watched from high ground, expecting to see the covered span snatched from its abutments.

In the onslaught of water, a barn above eased away from its foundations and came swirling down the Doe to smash full tilt against the bridge. For a few seconds it hung, crumbling, and then buckled under the sturdy trusses to

47. High-piered timbered tunnel perches above Red River at Port Royal, near Clarksville, Tennessee.

emerge in broken, bobbing pieces below.

For the upkeep of the old covered structure, the City of Elizabethton allots from $200 to $500 of municipal funds each year. Since the span is an ace tourist attraction, the money is considered well spent. A green-painted roof has replaced the original shingles, and the clapboards are kept painted with white lead. Four unique arched windows make for cheerier passage along the pedestrian walkway arranged along the side of the interior. An integral part of city life, it is estimated that a thousand cars use the bridge to cross the Doe during a twenty-four-hour period.

Though no longer in use, another surviving covered bridge perches on three tall stone piers, high above the Red River at Port Royal near Clarksville. The Howe-truss construction was not sufficient for its builder, J. C. McMillan, and he added a set of thin single arches for further reinforcement, after the bridge collapsed when nearly complete, in 1903.

Other existing covered bridges nestle in the valleys of the Great Smoky Region of East Tennessee, spanning mountain creeks with such names as Little Pigeon and Paint Rock.

Among the former roofed spans recorded in the state are those which were over the Harpeth River in Williamson County, and a number in the Clarksville vicinity, including a double-barreled Burr arch truss at Ringgold which dated back to 1856.

Unique in Tennessee was one of the very few

48. Post-Civil War sketch of covered bridge over Harpeth River at Franklin, Tennessee.

covered bridges to be built and used by a narrow-gauge railroad. This was the Little Doe River crossing near Hampton, Tennessee, on the East Tennessee & Western North Carolina Railroad. The little line with the big name was a favorite of excursionists and rail fans, who affectionately dubbed it "The Tweetsie," and enjoyed its mountain scenery. The last train chuffed over its three-foot rails in 1950, and with its passing went the covered bridge.

Tennessee even had a covered bridge built by George Washington. A neat span in the clapboarded style of the region, it spanned Sulphur Fork Creek on a rural road three miles south of Cedar Hill in Robertson County.

Though romanticists would have us believe otherwise, the Father of his Country never saw a covered bridge. He died in 1799, five years before the first American covered wooden truss was erected at Philadelphia.

The Sulphur Fork Creek bridge in Tennessee was of course built by another man entirely: George A. Washington, who fashioned its stout timbers a full century after the Declaration of Independence.

49. Former single span with horizontal siding was built near Cedar Hill, Tenn. by George (A.) Washington.

VII
KENTUCKY
Some Mountain Marvels

FORDS, primitive log bridges and makeshift ferries enabled pioneer Kentuckians to get across the streams whose courses slice the state. Literally hundreds of rivers and creeks tumble out of mountain hollows and tortuously meander, generally northward, eventually to blend their waters with those of the muddy Ohio.

The earliest routes between Kentucky settlements used the many navigable rivers, rather than crossed them, and it was not until turnpike days that bridges were erected with any thought of permanence.

Private enterprise provided cash for the pikes in hopes of a good return on the investment, and hired surveyors plotted routes where traffic could reasonably be expected. The little towns along the toll roads gradually grew into cities.

Typical of the roads-for-profit was the Maysville Pike, which stretched from the Ohio River

50. Civil War sketch shows Lewis Wernwag's double barrel crossing of Kentucky River at Boone's Knob.

southwest across the Licking River Valleys into the bluegrass country. To build its bridges the company hired a professional architect and covered-bridge builder, Lewis Wernwag of Harpers Ferry, Virginia. Already famed for his well-executed crossings of Atlantic seaboard rivers, Wernwag in 1830 took contracts for "several" bridges on the Maysville Pike in Kentucky, including the crossing of Stoner Creek in Paris. This was a big double-barreled bridge with three of Wernwag's unique and well-planned radial arches. Completed in 1833, the 160-foot structure stood for an even century.

At Boone's Knob, a crossing made famous by the illustrious Daniel, the German-born builder erected another of his wooden masterpieces. This too was a two-lane single arch, spanning a deep gorge between Winchester and Richmond, where the Kentucky River is flanked by high limestone cliffs.

Also of Wernwag's fabrication was a duplicate span some twenty miles downstream, south of Nicholasville. This one, carrying two lanes of roadway between its three trusses of carefully selected, massive timbers, had a clear span of 241 feet. Completed in 1838, the bridge bore the builder's name on its wide, squared portals.

A persistent rumor in Kentucky is that "Lewis Wernwag was a cripple and all his bridges were actually built by a brother named Thomas." With his services much in demand, the master builder and patentee subcontracted a number of his bridges to other builders. This is shown by records in West Virginia, Ohio and Indiana, where his name often appears only as "architect." Wernwag was obviously occupied a great deal as consultant for various works in progress. He may possibly have been incapacitated during the last years of his life, prior to his death in 1843, but no family account makes any allusion to it.

The exact sites of other Wernwag-built, superintended or designed bridges in Kentucky are uncertain. Three "possibles" stood over tributaries of Stoner Creek, south of Paris on the old turnpike to Winchester. Dating from 1831, these spans had truss members of poplar and siding of long-leaf yellow pine. Built on a sturdy queen-post plan, the three small bridges were constructed with special antimoisture housings at the chord ends, and the timbers were so arranged

as to give thorough ventilation throughout. As a result of these precautions, with only the shingle roofs replaced in later years by galvanized iron, all three spans gave service for 108 years.

Other main roads in central Kentucky crossed rivers by means of covered bridges. Eastbound drivers on what is now U.S. 60 rumbled through dark wooden tunnels over Big Bullskin Creek west of Shelbyville and over Benson Creek at Grafenburg before reaching the state capital at Frankfort by means of a passage through the big three-span arch bridge over the Kentucky River. This urban crossing had pedestrian walkways on either side.

The Civil War in 1861 brought galloping raiders and bridge burners into the border state of Kentucky. Loyalties were strongly divided, with recruits mustered into both Northern and Southern regiments. Towns like Cynthiana and Paris were captured and recaptured by the opposing forces, but fate saved the covered bridges of both.

Confederate General John Hunt Morgan was always a great one for daring forays against the enemy's lines of transport and communication. A compilation of covered bridges, both railroad and highway, which his men put to the torch would fill a lengthy page in the annals of the war.

In July 1862, Morgan appeared before Cynthiana, Kentucky, on one of his guerrilla raids. Union forces in the town consisted of the 18th Kentucky Regiment, led by Lieutenant Colonel John J. Landrum, plus a hundred Ohio volunteers sent down by train from Covington. Unaware of the Confederates' approach, Landrum sent the Ohio men, including two companies of Cincin-

51. Kentucky River Bridge with sidewalks served Frankfort.

52. Cynthiana, Kentucky was site of pitched battle with Morgan's Guerrilla Raiders in 1862. Bridge involved stood until 1946.

nati policemen, on to Paris.

The Federal troops soon found themselves cut off from any further reinforcements when the wily Morgan cut telegraph lines and burned bridges both above and below Cynthiana. Eight hundred strong, the guerrillas converged on Cynthiana from the south and spread out in prone positions along the river bank opposite the town. Landrum and his regiment perhaps might have set fire to the big bridge over the South Licking and saved the day. Instead, they preferred to exchange pot shots with the enemy across the river.

Not content with a standoff, the Confederate cavalrymen mounted a charge through the bridge. With rebel yells intensified by the hollow enclosure, they galloped down the long passage to debouch with flashing sabers among the startled Federals.

This daring sortie broke the Union defenses. Colonel Landrum and barely forty of his men were able to make good a retreat to Lexington, leaving both Cynthiana and Paris to the Southerners. Morgan tore down the courthouse flags, greeted old friends and supplied his men with fresh horses and arms. By the time reinforce-

ments arrived from the North, the Confederate guerrillas were gone, leaving the covered bridges in both towns surprisingly intact.

For another eighty years the 219-foot crossing of the South Licking continued to serve Cynthiana. Even after a new bridge was built nearby in 1944 there were hopes of its continued existence, due to its historical role in war. Unhappily, preservation plans came to nothing. Historic or not, there were just no funds available for saving and maintaining such a lengthy struc-

53. Runaway grass fire consumed Licking River Bridge on U.S. 62 at Claysville, Kentucky in 1953.

ture. In 1946 the big Burr arches were cut away and the bridge toppled into the river it had spanned since 1837.

One of Lewis Wernwag's giant Kentucky River spans also had Civil War connections. The lower gorge site became known as "Camp Nelson," named in honor of William Nelson, a naval officer who sent arms to "neutral" Kentucky. Established in 1863, the camp by the bridge was one of the principal staging grounds for Union troops and munitions used in mounting the Tennessee campaigns. It also served as a refuge for fugitive slaves and a main place of enlistment for Negro troops.

The close of hostilities saw a new period of bridge-building begun in Kentucky. Not only were war-ravaged bridges replaced, but new ones were erected, sometimes at spots where only a ferry had previously served. Big new bridges, for the most part of the later developed Howe-truss type, were built to span the Licking at places like Sherburne, Myers, Claysville, Falmouth and Butler. This last, the longest known covered bridge ever built in Kentucky, carried U.S. Route 27 across the Licking River on three spans with a total clear length of 456 feet. Built in 1870–71, it was damaged by the March flood of 1936 and replaced in September 1937.

A compilation of covered bridges in Kentucky showed approximately sixty-five still standing just previous to World War II. This number had shrunk to thirty-nine by 1952.

One bridge showed its age and effects of neglect in dramatic fashion. At Lair, in Harrison County south of Cynthiana, was a two-span Howe truss across the South Licking, dating from 1870. On July 11, 1946 the Kentucky State Highway Department solemnly condemned the bridge and so posted it. The bridge itself was quick to back the opinion of the experts. Just 30 minutes later a full half of it buckled and fell into the river with no warning.

During the past dozen years over half of the bridges of 1952 have disappeared. One of the last to serve a nationally numbered highway (U.S. 62) passed from the scene in September 1953, when a grass fire got away and consumed the Licking River bridge at Claysville. Owen County's last covered bridge, at Natlee, went up in flames in 1954, followed a year later by an

54. *Former Ruddell's Mills Bridge, once a landmark of Kentucky's Bourbon County.*

oddly fabricated truss over Dix River southwest of Lancaster. The state's latest bridge-burning by "persons unknown" took Bourbon County's fine old Ruddle's Mill Bridge in 1964.

The Louisville *Courier-Journal* reported that "nobody minded" when the string of three little covered bridges between North Middletown and Clintonville in Bourbon County were torn down and replaced by concrete in 1956. The county judge maintained that the continued existence of the trio of spans "caused accidents."

No cries of "Spare that bridge!" arose in 1954 when Montgomery County's sole survivor was replaced, or when Breckinridge County's lone covered span, long neglected, was unceremoniously razed with a tractor and attached cable.

Unique among some 12,000 bridges in the state, Kentucky's remaining covered wooden ones are all in the central and northeastern sections, and are located in a dozen counties.

Nearest the capital at Frankfort is the Switzer Bridge over the North Fork of Elkhorn Creek. Retired some years ago, this 120-foot Howe truss span has been retained as a local landmark.

Washington and Nelson counties still boast of three sizable covered bridges, all built on the well-known Burr arch plan and all over the century mark in age. Two big ones are situated over Chaplin River and Little Beech Creek on Kentucky Route 458. The first, stretching 276 feet in two spans, is Kentucky's longest covered bridge still standing. Both structures were built in Civil War days by Cornelius Barnes of Mt. Washington. Nearby at Sharpsville, Stephen Stone is credited with building a similar single-spanner about 1862.

55. *Attractive open-sided Howe Truss Bridge spanned Eagle Creek near Sanders, linking two Kentucky counties.*

56. *Retired but preserved, the bridge at Switzer still spans the north fork of Elkhorn Creek in Franklin County, Kentucky.*

The last of ten known roofed bridges in Bourbon County is located on the Colville Pike to the northeast of Paris. Nearby Fayette County has numerous little concrete and stone bridges named for famous Bluegrass-bred race horses, but no covered ones.

Located on streams not far from the Ohio River in the northeastern part of the state stand the balance of Kentucky's covered bridges. In Bracken County the bypassed Walcott Bridge is part of a picnic park. Robertson County's survivor is a Smith truss, built with 4×10-inch poplar timbers, with the added strength of a laminated arch. It is thought to be the work of the Bower Brothers, a team of builders from Troy, Ohio who used both the Smith plan and a patented one of their own.

Mason County's covered bridge near Dover is a primitive queenpost truss with heavy internal cross bracing. It appears to be very old, but has probably had several rebuildings.

In addition to two spans over Fox Creek on state highways south of Hillsboro and at Ringo's Mill, Fleming County can claim the state's only surviving example of the Town lattice truss. Called "White Bridge" because it was once kept in immaculate whitewashed splendor, this span over Sand Lick Creek was saved and re-erected at Goddard.

Also in Fleming County at the Bath County line stands Kentucky's most unusual and best preserved covered structure. This is Sherburne Bridge, which reaches 253 feet across the Licking

58. *Sherburne Bridge stretches high above Licking River. Reinforcing suspension cables were later concealed within.*

River in two unequal spans. Founded on massive, well-laid stone abutments and center pier, the bridge was erected in 1867 and is attributed to Isaac Kisker. Neat and trim, it is horizontally sided, with scalloped eave boards and twenty louvered windows.

In 1951, increased traffic on Kentucky Route 11 necessitated some drastic action at Sherburne. State highway engineers solved the problem in a unique manner. From steel framework posts erected at the portals and center pier they hung the components of a 2-span suspension bridge. Cables and hangers on either side encased the original Howe trusses and substantially added to both strength and durability. With this almost unprecedented combination, Sherburne became a covered suspension bridge, one of only a handful to have ever existed.

Today, one-way traffic through the old Kentucky landmark is regulated by a stop-light system. The new admonitions: TURN LIGHTS ON

57. *White Bridge has been re-erected over Sand Lick Creek at Goddard, Kentucky.*

are signs of the times, replacing old ones which once read: NO LOAFING ON BRIDGE.

Lewis County has an old privately maintained bridge northwest of Tollesboro at the Mackey-Hughes Farm. Greenup County retains two large bridges at Oldtown and Bennett's Mill, the latter a single-span Long truss bridge of 170 feet. This is a reminder that Colonel Stephen H. Long, the bridge inventor, once made his headquarters in Louisville, Kentucky, and promoted the use of his patents while stationed there.

Finally, on the West Virginia border is Lawrence County, where the old red Yatesville Bridge over Blaine Creek is bypassed and retained. Also in this county is Kentucky's shortest (42 feet) and youngest (1924) covered bridge.

Photographer-writers John and Sue Thierman of Lexington found this bridge by chance in 1952. At a crossroad store in Fallsburg they casually asked: "Any covered bridges around here?"

A tall, lean fellow spoke up. "Over on East Fork," he volunteered. "Me and my brother built it."

Thus it happened that the Thiermans got to talk to and photograph a covered-bridge builder, along with his handiwork.

Back in 1924 Magistrate B. V. Shortridge had a 11,000-acre tract along the East Fork of Little Sandy River, but no easy means of access. His son-in-law, John Riffe, took the contract to build a bridge. Shortridge drew up plans for the structure and Riffe got his brother George to help. After the county poured concrete abutments the brothers hauled in five big 40-foot oak beams for stringers, fashioned kingposts for trusswork,

59. Older signs admonished passers-by at State Highway Bridge over Licking River at Sherburne, Kentucky.

nailed on weatherboarding and put a corrugated tin roof over all.

Only when the state's total number of covered bridges had dwindled to eighteen did Kentuckians come to the realization that much of their historical heritage was going by the board. Sparked by Paul L. Atkinson, then of Newport, the Kentucky Covered Bridge Association came into being in 1964. Group and individual letters to state and local authorities, plus personal appeals to Kentucky's Governor, gave much publicity to the ends of bridge preservation. The struggle to save most of the covered bridges continues today in the Bluegrass State, and it appears as though the remaining timbered tunnels, barring flood or fire, have a good chance of an indefinite further existence.

VIII

All Gone Now

THERE are records of covered bridges, either highway or railway, that exist or existed in forty-two of the fifty United States.

In the South, only Florida and Louisiana have never had covered bridges other than those of the replica or "private garden" variety.

Though no covered bridges remain within their borders today, three other southern states can contribute to the annals of Dixie wooden bridge engineering history.

MISSISSIPPI--Prisoners and Apathy

THE STORY of covered bridges in Mississippi is nearly as shadowy as the old spans themselves. Over the years the hooded crossings were a feature only of scattered localities, their building doubtless influenced by the carpenter-contractors who were familiar with this type of bridge.

Perhaps stemming from its early acceptance in neighboring Alabama, the Town lattice appears to have been the most popular of known covered bridges in the state. Lowndes and Monroe counties in eastern Mississippi were liberally peppered with these Yankee-inspired contraptions, and they served well. Usually the bridge proper was only over the stream's main channel, joined to dry land by open wooden trestling on either side, set on piles above the marshy river bottomland.

In 1838 Robert Jamison established a grist mill on Luxapalila Creek in Lowndes County, near the present village of Steens. Along with a store and smithy, the mill became a magnet for farmers from miles around. Jamison, a perceptive businessman, thought it well worth the expense and the use of his slave labor to put up seven covered bridges over the Luxapalila and other streams in the vicinity of Steens. It was no accident that all these bridges were on direct roads leading to the Jamison store and mill.

In adjacent Monroe County it was a similar story, with bridges over the Buttahatchie and Tombigbee to serve roads that converged on the town of Aberdeen. Builders in this region used varied techniques to provide sturdy underpinning for their wooden spans. The James Creek Bridge south of Aberdeen was mounted on four high blocks of concrete, one based at each corner. Farther on was the Buttahatchie River crossing, whose builders Alf Booth and Rube Irvin preferred massive tubular concrete caissons for abutments. To the east of the county seat was still another crossing, heavily braced with massive buttresses. This one perched above the Buttahatchie on well-fashioned piers of red brick. Allowed to deteriorate in their declining years, the covered spans of this region were often derisively referred to by natives as "those old shanty bridges."

Over near the winding Mississippi River between Vicksburg and Natchez was another "nest" of half a dozen covered bridges in Claiborne County. These served the roads in the vicinity

60. *Brick piers were novel feature of Buttahatchie River Bridge east of Aberdeen, Mississippi.*

61. *Former Lattice Bridge on concrete pillars over James Creek south of Aberdeen, Mississippi.*

62. *Concrete piling kept old Lattice Bridge out of the Buttahatchie River near Aberdeen, Miss. until 1931.*

of Port Gibson, high, narrow spans with multiple kingpost trusses. The last one, over Clark's Creek on Lower Brandywine Road, was built in 1877 and came down in 1953.

Up in Lafayette County a bypassed lattice structure over the Yacona River continued in existence after the channel of the river below it was changed. As the "sole remaining covered bridge in Mississippi," its final years were the 1950's. Reached by a road made almost impassable by mud and encroaching vines, it was used only by neighboring fieldhands to obtain a bit of cool shade.

Mississippi had another covered bridge a century ago, prominently located over the Pearl River at the state capital of Jackson. Because of its tragic connections, modern historians have chosen to forget and even deny its existence. Nevertheless, there really was a covered bridge at Jackson, recorded because it served in the unusual capacity of prison for 401 Union soldiers.

63. *Last of a group of covered bridges which stood near Port Gibson, Miss. This one over Clark's Creek came down in 1953.*

64. *Prison Bridge over Pearl River at Jackson, Mississippi into which captured Union soldiers were jammed in 1863.*

A terse account of the Pearl River bridge-prison has been left by Colonel Thomas C. Fletcher of the Missouri Wide Awake Zouaves, who was wounded and captured by the Confederates during an assault on Chickasaw Bluffs near Vicksburg.

After his capture on December 29, 1862, Colonel Fletcher was first thrown into the Vicksburg jail for a month. Then, along with twenty other officers, he was removed to Jackson, "and thrust into the old rickety ruin of a bridge which was yet standing above water, the remaining part having fallen down."

The Confederate jailers used considerable ingenuity in coverting the old lattice bridge into a virtually escape-proof lockup. Isolated, and perched on stiltlike piling, its ends were tightly boarded and armed guards patrolled the bank and river below.

Twenty-one officers within the confines of a single span of covered bridge perhaps 100 feet long by 18 feet wide might have been tolerable, but soon *three hundred and eighty* more Union prisoners were jammed in with them. Unable to lie, or even sit down except by taking turns for limited periods, the men stood propped against the walls and each other. For the entire month of February, with the wind whistling between the planks of the floor and weatherboarding, the prisoners shuffled a few feet at a time and endured their misery. There was no light, and very little food.

Libby in Richmond and Andersonville in Georgia were more notorious, but Mississippi's bridge-prison at Jackson was no less a horrible place of incarceration. Almost every day two or three men died on their feet. Pried from the gaunt and hollow-eyed mass of humanity within the bridge, they were carried out to lie unburied for days on the river bank.

Colonel Fletcher himself prepared a sketch of the prison, later published in *Harper's Weekly.* The 401 men in the bridge, reduced by death to three-quarters of their original number, were eventually transferred, perhaps to even worse

prisons, and their officers exchanged. The infamous bridge was burned by Grant and Sherman's troops during the capture and sacking of Jackson in May 1863.

ARKANSAS--A Hardy Specimen

65. *The last to stand, and one of the very few covered bridges ever built in Arkansas was Two Bayou Bridge southwest of Camden.*

ON A ROAD through the swampy woods southwest of Camden stood Two Bayou Bridge. This span had a well-formed but simply constructed Howe truss reaching about three-quarters of the height of the bridge, with additional framework and cross bracing to support a roof and siding. It was built "about 1860."

The covering was a novelty for Arkansas, and this was one of the very few wooden bridges in the state known to have been afforded the extra protection. That the added time, trouble and expense was worthwhile is shown by the fact that the bridge stood without anything more than normal maintenance until bypassed by U.S. Route 79 in the 1940's. This was quite a tribute to the efficacy of wood protection at a notably damp bridge site.

Even after the shingled roof and old board siding were stripped from the bridge and it stood abandoned, the span stoutly refused to tumble down for nearly ten years.

TEXAS--Sure We Did!

COVERED BRIDGES in Texas? It would seem improbable that there ever were any. And yet, why not? Despite its vast size and apparently endless plains, the state had stands of good timber and plenty of settlers from regions both North and South where the covered bridge was already established as a very commonplace structure. For most crossings, early Texans used ferries, fords and simple trestle bridges. But now

and then on an important road a more adequate bridge was needed, particularly in times of flood.

There have been no covered bridges in Texas for over half a century. And the average Texan, when queried, will usually smile indulgently as he shakes his head. But in recent years diligent research has tracked down rumors, true and false, of covered bridges that once did exist in Texas.

66. *A Texas rarity. Covered bridge built in 1854 to span the San Marcos River two ~~miles~~ west of Gonzales.*

There were at least five of them, remembered distinctly by people who grew up in the 1880's and '90's. Mrs. W. G. Achenbach of Amarillo recalled two, one on either side of McKinney in Collin County, and a third at Weston. These spanned the east and west forks of the Trinity River and were painted a dark red. A member of the Christian Church, Mrs. Achenbach was baptized in the East Fork of the Trinity at a beautiful spot just beyond one of the old bridges.

Farther downstate, a Californian recalled a covered bridge of his youth, spanning the San Marcos River near Victoria, Texas. Over the same river, two miles west of Gonzales, was still another Texas covered bridge, clear in the memory of Mrs. Joe B. Dunning of Dallas.

Sparked by the interest, the Gonzales *Inquirer* not only found something of the history of their San Marcos bridge, but unearthed two pictures to prove that its former existence was no hazy, idle memory.

Pointing out the rarity of covered bridges in Texas, an old piece in the *Inquirer* called the span "one of the most unique bridge structures ever constructed." Two huge stone piers were built on either side of the San Marcos, to put the span high above any flood stage of the river. The bridge itself, well over a hundred feet long, was built in 1854 by John Mooney. Timber was hand-hewn from selected trees along the river banks, and floated downstream to the bridge site to be fashioned into trusses by Mooney's slaves.

The finished San Marcos bridge stood up high and proud above the countryside, reached by open wooden approaches. Picnics on the bank of the river were often continued beneath its friendly shelter when it rained. During some seasons of the year traffic was so infrequent that weary travelers occasionally made camp inside the bridge when the weather was wet or cold.

After fifty years of useful service, Mooney's unique Texas landmark was replaced by an iron span built alongside. Its prominent position can still be well imagined, for despite attempts to dynamite and remove them, the massive stone piers which supported the old wooden bridge are still standing today.

67. *After a half century of service, the San Marcos Bridge near Gonzales, Texas gets an iron successor in 1904.*

APPENDIX I – WHAT MAKES A BRIDGE

The following is a summary of two chapters from *Covered Bridges of the Northeast*, published in 1957 as the first volume in a projected series on America's great wooden bridges and their builders. R. S. A.

A bridge is defined simply as a structure erected to furnish a roadway over a depression or an obstacle; that is, over valleys or chasms, over water or other roads.

In general, bridges are supported in four ways: they are 1) propped from below—as by piling or trestles bedded in the bottom of a river or a defile; 2) carried for short distances by their own rigidity—as by stout logs, steel girders or prestressed concrete slabs; 3) held by the action of triangular (plus sometimes curved) arrangements of wooden or metal members, pressing against themselves as they press against land masses—as by trusses, or 4) hung from towers or upward projecting land masses—as in suspension bridges.

This book is concerned with the third classification, that of *truss* bridges. To understand them, though, it is necessary to start with the simple *stringer* crossings of the first group.

Man's first bridge was a stringer: he simply felled a tree growing on a riverbank so that it spanned the gap to the opposite bank. Then he teetered across it. Later he refined his invention by placing another log parallel to the first one and laying billets of wood across both of them to form a wider walkway, thus:

But what if a stream was wide? The longer the logs, the more likely they were to sag. The answer, developed centuries ago in Central Europe, was to cut two logs, press their butts into the banks (the shore foundations, called *abutments*) so that they met at an obtuse angle under the midpoint of the stringers; these were *braces*. Later a parallel stringer was added to close the open side of the triangle and keep the arms of the braces from shifting. The new stringer below was called the *lower chord;* the original one was the *upper chord.*

This combination of chords and braces was the first truss: a triangular system of timbers so devised that each member helped to support another, and together they supported whatever weight was put upon the whole.

Bridge building developed with piecemeal innovations during the Dark Ages, culminating in a virtually slipproof support when a centerpost was introduced to reach from the apex of the triangle to the midpoint of the lower chord, and so form this *kingpost* truss:

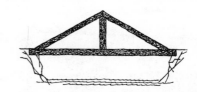

The kingpost was the earliest formal bridge truss design and it employed a primary engineering principle: a triangle will hold its shape under a load until its side members or its joints are crushed.

It is well to stop here and emphasize that the actual bridge consists of two trusses, one on each side; therefore the roadway—and, in covered spans, the roof and weatherboarding—has little to do with the bridge's basic structural efficiency. The description can be streamlined further by the reasonable practice of including the two sides in referring to the truss of a bridge.

The first kingpost truss was built under the stringers (forming a *deck* truss), where it was highly vulnerable to flood and ice. Then some inspired builder realized that kingpost triangles were equally effective when erected above the stringers (making a *through* truss). This rather oversimplified diagram and its explanation tell why:

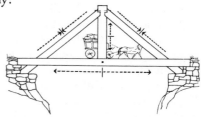

Although seemingly inelastic, the diagonal braces—called *compression members*—are subjected to squeeze as a load passes over the bridge. Meanwhile the same native flexibility allows the centerpost and lower chord—the *tension members*—to be pulled downward. So, if its truss is abutted properly into the banks, a bridge shoves harder against the land with the more weight that is put upon it, and the interaction of its truss members actually makes it stronger when it carries a load.

The whole matter of shifts and variations in stress is extremely complex and wasn't described fully until 1847. By then the wooden truss had undergone many elaborations.

A natural development was this *queenpost* truss, in which the peak of the kingpost triangle was replaced by a horizontal crosspiece to allow the base to be longer and span wider streams:

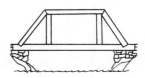

The next amplification produced the even longer *multiple kingpost,* a series of uprights with all braces inclined toward the centerpost:

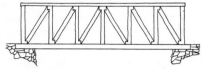

A river that was neither too swift nor too deep could be crossed by supporting such an elongated truss with one or more natural or man-made piers rising from the streambed. In a *multi-span* bridge of this sort the number of spans is one more than the number of intermediate supports between abutments.

Still, sometimes the character of a river made piers impossible: then a corollary design was used which combined an arch with a multiple kingpost. The earliest known drawings of the basic multiple kingpost and arch combinations were published in 1570 by Andrea Palladio. By that time, too, builders had begun to side and roof their bridges, simply to prevent the wooden trusses from rotting.

From the mid-1500's until the nineteenth century wooden bridge design lay dormant. Then came America's trio of pioneer builders—Palmer, Burr and Wernwag—to use the arch and kingpost for spans of a size hitherto undreamed of.

Timothy Palmer's design, patented in 1797, had auxiliary trusswork digging deep into the face of the abutments below the braced double arch:

PALMER

This was his general plan for the nation's first covered bridge, finished at Philadelphia in 1805.

A year earlier, Theodore Burr had patented this arch-truss:

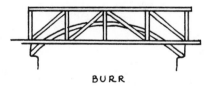

BURR

Each of its sides was a great arch sandwiched between two conventional kingpost arrangements, and its roadway, unlike Palmer's, was level. Burr used this plan for his all-time record single span (360′ 4″) at McCall's Ferry, Pennsylvania.

Flared kingposts bracing a double arch were the hallmarks of the best of Lewis Wernwag's many designs, which began with The Colossus in 1812. The one most popularly accepted looked like this:

WERNWAG

A wholly American truss plan appeared in 1820, ideal for cheap, strong bridges that were easy to build. It was this "lattice mode" by Ithiel Town:

TOWN

Merely a series of overlapping triangles with no arches or uprights, it resembled a crisscross garden fence that could be "built by the mile and cut off by the yard" to support spans up to 200 feet in length. It was his new approach to the use of the basic unadorned triangle that made Town's truss unique.

A decade later Col. Stephen H. Long introduced this panel truss, a series of boxed X's with three or more panels comprising the entire truss:

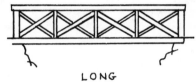

LONG

In 1840 William Howe brought about a bridge building revolution by introducing an iron rod into wooden trusses. Howe's design unabashedly copied the Long panel, replacing its uprights with iron tie-rods that could be readily adjusted with nuts and turnbuckles:

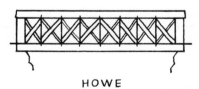

HOWE

Thus he coped with the major weakness of wood in bridge construction: the elasticity which allows strength-giving compression also permits the joints of an upright tension member to pull apart under heavy loads.

The Howe truss became the favored railroad bridge across America, and even influenced bridge construction in Europe and Asia. With it, wooden bridge building reached its peak; and with it the transition was made to bridges built of iron and steel.

APPENDIX II: Tabulation of Existing Covered Bridges

There have been a number of covered bridges erected in recent years. These range from tiny little spans in private backyard gardens to full-size replicas in urban housing developments. With so many popping up, there is danger in overlooking the merits of actual and authentic covered bridges, whose retention and continued existence would seem a far more worthy cause.

Until some kind of national authentication committee of covered bridge fanciers is established, any tabulation of existing covered bridges will depend on the feelings of the list-maker as to what constitutes a covered bridge.

The following list is accurate and complete as far as compilation has been currently possible. In the fast-changing world of covered bridges there will quickly be deletions, corrections and even an occasional addition. R.S.A.

LOCATION	NAME	OWNER	STREAM	Spans & Length	Date	TYPE	BUILDER, etc.
ALABAMA							
BLOUNT COUNTY							
5 mi SW of Oneonta			Dub. Br. of Locust Fork	1— 84		Town	
2½ mi NW of Cleveland	Swan		Locust Fork	3—305		Town	
1 mi S of Nectar			Locust Fork	4—371		Town	
5 mi N of Oneonta	Horton's Mills		Calvert Prong	2—204		Town	70 ft. high
CALHOUN COUNTY							
3½ mi SE of Wellington		T	Tallahatchee Creek	1— 61		Mod—KP	
Near Oxford	Mellon		Choccolocco Creek	1— 86		Mod—KP	
SE of Coldwater			Coldwater Creek	1— 59		Mod—KP	
COLBERT COUNTY							
3½ mi SW of Cherokee	Buzzard Roost		Buzzard Roost Creek	1— 94	c. 1860	Town	Allsboro Rd.
COOSA COUNTY							
SW of Alexander City	Thomas Store		Br. of Oakachoy Creek	1— 60	1916	Mod—QP	
CULLMAN COUNTY							
NW of Clarkson		T	Crooked Creek	2—270		Town	
ETOWAH COUNTY							
Keener		T	Big Wills Creek	3—366		Steel Truss Columns	
Reece City		T	Little Wills Creek	1—100		Town	Moved to Noccalula Falls, nr. Gadsden
LEE COUNTY							
2 mi SW of Yarbrough			Hallawakee Creek	2—140		Town	
2 mi NE of Salem			Waccoochee Creek	1— 58		Town	
SUMTER COUNTY							
Livingston	Bellamy	T	Alamuchee Creek	1— 82	1861	Town	Capt. W.A.C. Jones. Orig. over Sucarnoo-chee R. Moved 1924
TALLADEGA COUNTY							
SE of Talladega	Riddle's Mill		Talladega Creek	1—100		Town	
Kymulga		T	Talladega Creek	1—100		Town	
GEORGIA							
BANKS COUNTY							
N of Maysville	Perkins		Hickory Level Creek	1— 72		Queenpost	
E of Gillsville			Drainage for Grove Cr.	1— 63		Town	Remainder of twins brought from Broad R.
E of Lula			Grove Creek	1— 35		Kingpost	
E of Hollingsworth	(nr. Urena)		Middle Fork, Broad R.	1— 92		Queenpost	
NE of Commerce	(nr. Salem Church)		Br. of Grove Creek	1— 46		Kingpost	
BARROW-JACKSON COUNTIES							
W of Braselton	Thompson's Mill (off Rte. 211)		Mulberry River	2—219		Town	
BARTOW COUNTY							
Euharlee			Euharlee Creek	1—116	1886	Town	
COBB COUNTY							
4½ mi E of Marietta	Paper Mill Road		Sope's Creek	2—		Town	Orig. 1 span
DAWSON COUNTY							
W of Dawsonville			Amicalola Creek	1— 84	c.1904	Town	

LOCATION	NAME	OWNER	STREAM	Spans & Length	Date	TYPE	BUILDER, etc.
DEKALB COUNTY							
Stone Mountain Memorial Park			Arm of Stone Mountain Lake	3—162	c.1890	Town	Former "College Ave. Bridge," N. Fk. Oconee R. in Athens, Clarke Co. Moved here 1965
EARLY COUNTY							
N of Hilton			Coheelee Creek	2— 96	1883	Kingpost	J. W. Baughman
5 mi SW of Blakely			Sowhatchee Creek	2— 96	1883	Queenpost	J. W. Baughman
FORSYTH COUNTY							
5 mi N of Ducktown	Poole Mill		Sittingdown Creek	1— 90		Town	
FRANKLIN COUNTY							
S of Carnesville	Cromer's Mill		Nails Creek	1—132		Town	
HALL COUNTY							
W of Candler			Walnut Creek	1— 48		Kingpost	
HARRIS COUNTY							
Callaway Gardens	Harmony Road		Mt. Oak Creek (Diversion Ditch)	60		Town	Former Harmony Rd. Bridge, Troup Co. Moved 1965. Cut down from 173 ft.
JACKSON COUNTY							
4 mi E of Maysville	Hurricane Grove		North Oconee River	1—127		Town	
MADISON-OGLETHORPE COUNTIES							
SE of Comer	Watson Mill		Broad River	4—236	1886	Town	Site of new state park, 1969
MERIWETHER COUNTY							
4 mi SE of Alvaton			White Oak Creek	1— 80	c.1880	Long	
4½ mi SE of Gay	Imlac		Big Red Oak Creek	1—116		Town	
OCONEE COUNTY							
5 mi SW of Watkinsville	Elder's Mill Road		Rose Creek	1— 75		Town	
OGLETHORPE COUNTY							
SE of Smithonia			Big Clouds Creek	2—168		Town	
STEPHENS COUNTY-OCONEE COUNTY, S.C.							
N of Toccoa	Prather's		Tugaloo River	2—158		Town	Also listed under South Carolina
TROUP COUNTY							
NW of La Grange	Neely Road		White Water Creek	1— 79		Town	
UPSON COUNTY							
SE of Thomaston	Hootenville or Allen Rd.		Achumpkee Creek	1— 96		Town	
WALTON COUNTY							
2½ mi NE of Campton			Apalachee River	1—104		Town	
WHITE COUNTY							
NE of Nacoochee			Chickamauga Creek	1— 33		Kingpost	

KENTUCKY

LOCATION	NAME	OWNER	STREAM	Spans & Length	Date	TYPE	BUILDER, etc.
BATH-FLEMING COUNTIES							
Sherburne			Licking River	2—253	1867 -68	Howe w/Modern Suspension Enclosed	Isaac Kisker
BOURBON COUNTY							
NE of Paris	Colville Pike		Hinkston Creek	1—120	1877	Multiple-Kingpost	
BRACKEN COUNTY							
NW of Brooksville	Walcott		Locust Creek	1— 69		Comb. King & Queenpost	
FLEMING COUNTY							
Ringo's Mill			Fox Creek	1— 84	1867	Multiple-Kingpost	
4 mi S of Hillsboro			Fox Creek	1— 86		Multiple-Kingpost	
Goddard	White		Sand Lick Creek	1— 63		Town	
FRANKLIN COUNTY							
Switzer		T	No. Fork, Elkhorn Cr.	1—120		Howe	
GREENUP COUNTY							
N of Lynn	Bennetts Mill		Tygarts Creek	1—170	c.1855 -56	Long	B.F. & Pramley Bennett
Oldtown			Little Sandy River	2—178		Multiple-Kingpost	
LAWRENCE COUNTY							
NW of Louisa	Yatesville		Blaine Creek	1—128		Howe	
5 mi NW of Fallsburg			E. Fk. of Little Sandy R.	1— 42	1924	Modified KP	John & Geo. Riffe
LEWIS COUNTY							
4½ mi NW of Tollesboro	Mackey-Hughes	P	Cabin Creek	1—114	1867	Multiple KP w/ laminated arches	
MASON COUNTY							
East of Dover			Lees Creek or Lick Run	1— 63	c.1845	Queenpost variant w/ x braces	Rebuilt c. 1920
NELSON COUNTY							
Andy L. Ramsour			Chaplin River	2—276	1862	Burr	Cornelius Barnes
ROBERTSON COUNTY							
N of Blue Lick Springs			Johnson Creek	2—108	1878	Smith w/ laminated arch.	Bower Bros.

LOCATION	NAME	OWNER	STREAM	Spans & Length	Date	TYPE	BUILDER, etc.
WASHINGTON COUNTY							
Sharpsville			Chaplin River	1—145	1862	Burr	Stephen Stone
Mooresville			Little Beech Creek	2—210	1865	Burr	Cornelius Barnes

NORTH CAROLINA

LOCATION	NAME	OWNER	STREAM	Spans & Length	Date	TYPE	BUILDER, etc.
CATAWBA COUNTY							
2 mi E of Claremont	Bunker Hill	T	Lyles Creek	1— 80	1895	Haupt	
RANDOLPH COUNTY							
2 mi W of Pisgah		T	Branch of Little River	3— 54	c.1920	Warren adapt.	J. J. Welsh
13 mi NW of Asheboro	Skeen Mill	T	Br. of Little Uwharrie R.	1— 72	c.1901	Town & QP	Hezekiah Andrews

SOUTH CAROLINA

LOCATION	NAME	OWNER	STREAM	Spans & Length	Date	TYPE	BUILDER, etc.
McCORMICK COUNTY							
West of Troy	Long Cane Church	T	Long Cane Creek	1—163		Howe	John E. Bradley
OCONEE COUNTY-STEPHENS COUNTY, GEORGIA							
West of Westminster	Prather's		Tugaloo River	2—158		Town	Also listed under Georgia
OCONEE-PICKENS COUNTIES							
Eastatoe—Jocassee	Chapman's		Keowee River	1—128	1922	Howe variant	James Craig

TENNESSEE

LOCATION	NAME	OWNER	STREAM	Spans & Length	Date	TYPE	BUILDER, etc.
CARTER COUNTY							
Elizabethton			Doe River	1—134	1885	Howe	
GREENE COUNTY							
6 mi S of Midway	Chucky		Little Chucky Creek	1— 58	1920	Modified QP	
KNOX COUNTY							
3 mi SW of Blaine	Brice		Big Flat Creek	1—101	1876	Howe	
MONTGOMERY COUNTY							
J.C. McMillan			Red River	2—200	1904	Howe w/ arch	
SCOTT COUNTY							
1¼ mi SW of Capital Hill	Winona		Paint Rock Creek	3—103	c.1900	Queenpost	
SEVIER COUNTY							
7 mi E of Sevierville	Harrisburg		Little Pigeon River	1— 64	c.1890	Queenpost	

Glossary

ABUTMENT—The shore foundation upon which a bridge rests, usually built of stone but sometimes of bedrock, wood, iron or concrete.

ARCH—A structural curved timber, or arrangement of timbers, to support a bridge, usually used in covered bridges together with a truss. Thus a *supplemental* or *auxiliary arch* is one which assists a truss and forms an arch-truss; a *true arch* bridge is entirely dependent upon the arch for support.

BENT—An arrangement of timbers resembling a saw-horse which is placed under a bridge at right angles to the stringers, sometimes used as a temporary scaffolding in building a covered bridge. Also to support light, open approaches, weak or damaged bridges, and sometimes as a substitute for abutments or piers.

BRACE—A diagonal timber in a truss which slants toward the midpoint of the bridge.

CHORD—The top (*upper chord*) or bottom (*lower chord*) member or members of a bridge truss, usually formed by the stringers; may be a single piece or a series of long joined pieces.

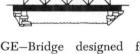

COMBINATION BRIDGE—Bridge designed for both highway and railroad traffic; also, a structure made with two types of trusses or combining features of two different trusses.

COMPRESSION MEMBER—A timber or other truss member which is subjected to squeeze. Often a diagonal member, such as a brace (q.v.) or counterbrace (q.v.).

CORBEL—In covered bridges, a solid piece of wood —mainly for decoration—which projects from the portal and assists in supporting the overhanging roof. Also, on a larger scale, a solid timber at the angle of an abutment (or pier) and lower chord to lend extra support.

COUNTERBRACE—A diagonal timber in a truss which slants away from the midpoint of the bridge (opposite from brace, q.v.).

DECK TRUSS—A type of bridge where the traffic, usually railroad, uses the roof on top of the truss as a roadbed; sometimes also carries traffic inside, between the trusses.

DOUBLE-BARRELED BRIDGE—Common designation for a covered bridge with two lanes; the divider can be a third truss or structural part of the bridge, or it can be a simple partition.

FACE OF ABUTMENT—The side of the abutment toward the center of the stream.

FALSEWORK—See SCAFFOLDING.

FLOOR BEAM—Transverse beam between bottom chords of trusses on which longitudinal joists are laid.

JOIST—Timbers laid longitudinally on the floor beams of a bridge and over which the floor planking is laid.

KEY—Piece, often a wedge, inserted in a joint such as a mortise-and-tenon to tighten the connection. Sometimes called a *fid*.

LAMINATED ARCH—A series of planks bolted together to form an arc; constructed in such a manner that the boards are staggered to give extra strength.

LATERAL BRACING—An arrangement of timbers between the two top chords or between the two bottom chords of bridge trusses to keep the trusses spaced apart correctly and to insure their strength. The arrangement may be very simple, or complex.

MORTISE, (n)—Cavity made in wood to receive a tenon. (v)—To join or fasten securely by using a mortise and tenon.

PANEL—Rectangular section of truss included between two vertical posts and the chords. A *panel system* is made up of three or more panels.

PARAPETS—Low masonry stone walls on either side of the section of roadway leading directly into a bridge. Common in Pennsylvania.

PATENTED TRUSS—Any one of the truss types for which United States patents have been granted, such as Burr, Town, Long, Howe, etc., trusses.

PIER—An intermediate foundation between abutments, built in the streambed, for additional support for the bridge. May be made of stone, concrete, wood, etc.

PILE—Heavy timber, often a peeled log, sunk vertically into the streambed to provide a foundation when the bottom is unreliable. Piling can be used as a base for abutments and piers, or the bridge can be built directly upon piling.

PORTAL—General term for the entrance or exit of a covered bridge; also used to refer to the boarded section of either end under the roof.

POST—Upright or vertical timber in a bridge truss; *centerpost* is the vertical timber in the center of a truss; *endpost* is the vertical timber at either end of the truss.

RAFTER—One of a series of relatively narrow beams joined with its opposite number to form an inverted V to support the roof boards of a bridge.

SCAFFOLDING—Light, temporary wooden platforms built to assist in the erection of a bridge. Sometimes called *falsework*.

SECONDARY CHORD—Single or joined timbers lying between upper and lower chords and parallel to them, giving added strength to the truss.

SHELTER PANEL—The first panel at each end of both trusses of a panel-truss bridge, often boarded on the inside to protect the timbers from moisture blowing through the portals.

SHIP'S KNEE—A short timber bent at a right angle used inside a covered bridge between a truss and upper lateral bracing to increase rigidity. Similar to a corbel (q.v.) but heavier and not decorative. Sometimes called *knee brace*.

SIMPLE TRUSS—An elementary bridge truss, such as kingpost or queenpost; not so large or complex as the patented trusses.

SKEW-BACK—A jog or incline in the face of an abutment to receive the end of a chord or an arch.

SKEWED BRIDGE—A bridge built diagonally across a stream.

SPAN—The length of a bridge between abutments or piers. *Clear span* is the distance across a bridge having no intermediate support, and measured from the face of one abutment to the face of the other. The length usually given is for the *truss span*, i.e., the length between one endpost of the truss and the other, regardless of how far the truss may overreach the actual abutment. Bridges of more than one span are called *multi-span bridges*.

SPLICE—A method of joining timbers, especially end-to-end, by means of a scarf or other joint, sometimes with keys or wedges inserted to give additional strength and stability to the joint. A *splice-clamp* is a metal or wooden clamp designed to hold two spliced timbers together.

STRINGER (or STRING-PIECE)—A longitudinal member of a truss which may be made up of either one single timber, in comparatively short bridges, or a series of timbers spliced end-to-end in longer bridges. Most evident in the chords (q.v.) which often go by this name.

SUSPENSION ROD (or HANGER ROD or SUSPENDER)—Iron rod usually found in arch bridges or in connection with auxiliary arches added to older bridges; attached from arch to floor beams to aid in supporting the roadway.

TENON—A tongue shaped at the end of a timber to fit into a mortise and so form a joint.

TENSION MEMBER—Any timber or rod of a truss which is subjected to pull, or stretch.

TIE-ROD—Iron rod used as integral vertical member in some truss bridges to replace wooden posts between upper and lower chords. Bridge members could be tightened by adjusting nuts against washers on the ends of the rods. Their use marked the first step in transition from wooden bridges to bridges made entirely of iron.

TREENAILS—Wooden pins which are driven into holes of slightly smaller diameter to pin members of lattice trusses together (pronounced "trunnels").

TRESTLE—A braced framework built up from the streambed to support a bridge.

THROUGH TRUSS—A covered bridge in which traffic uses a roadway laid on the lower chords between the trusses. Most covered bridges are through trusses.

TRUSS—An arrangement of members, such as timbers, rods, etc., in a rigid form so united that they support each other plus whatever weight is put upon the whole. Covered bridge trusses, including arch-trusses, employ a triangle or a series of combined triangles. *Truss* can designate just one side of a bridge, generally is used as meaning the combined sides.

TURNBUCKLE—A metal loop fashioned with a screw at one end and a swivel at the other, used in some covered bridge trusses to tighten iron rods and thus overcome sagging.

WEB—A truss design (such as Town lattice) in which timbers crisscross each other. A lattice truss, or a truss designed with overlapping panels, may be called a *web system*.

WEDGE—See KEY.

WINDBRACING—Inside timbers extending from a point on a truss to the ridgepole to attach the roof more firmly to the sides of the bridge.

Selected Bibliography

Cooper, Theodore. *American Railroad Bridges*. New York [1889].

Edwards, Llewellyn N. *A Record of History and Evolution of Early American Bridges*. Orono, Me., 1959.

Fletcher, Robert, and Snow, J. P. *A History of the Development of Wooden Bridges, Paper #1864*. American Society of Civil Engineers, New York, 1934.

Kirby, Richard S., and Laurson, Philip G. *The Early Years of Modern Civil Engineering*. New Haven, 1932.

Long, Col. S. H. *Description of Col. Long's Bridges*. Concord, N.H., 1836.

Pittinger, Rev. William. *Capturing a Locomotive*. Philadelphia, 1883.

Sellers, Charles Coleman. *Charles Willson Peale*. 1947.

Sloane, Eric. *American Barns and Covered Bridges*. New York, 1954.

Tyrrell, Henry G. *History of Bridge Engineering*. Chicago, 1911.

Wells, Rosalie. *Covered Bridges in America*. New York, 1931.

Also:

Covered Bridge Topics. National Society for the Preservation of Covered Bridges, Inc., 1942– —.

CRVCBS Bulletin. Connecticut River Valley Covered Bridge Society, 1958– —.

World Guide to Covered Bridges. National Society for the Preservation of Covered Bridges, Inc., Boston, 1965.

Index

Aberdeen (Miss.) 2, 38, 39
Alabama, Covered Bridges −22
Alamuchee Creek Bridge near Bellamy (Ala.) −26
Albany, Flint River Bridge (Ga.) −17
Allen's Bridge (S.C.) −**13,** 14
Andersonville Prison (Ga.) −41
Andrews (James J., Secret Agent) Raid, 1862 −18
Andrews, Hezekiah −7
Arab, (Ala.) −22
Arkansas, Covered Bridges −42
Armstrong, W.H., Bridge Designer −20
Asheboro (N.C.) −5,6
Ashley River (Charleston, S.C.) −10
Athens (Ga.) −20, 21
Augusta (Ga.) −16

Baldwin County (Ga.) −17
Banks County (Ga.) −17, 20
Barnes, Cornelius, Bridge Builder −34
Baughman, J.W., Bridge Builder of Early Co. (Ga.) −17
Beane Mill Bridge −8
Bear Creek Bridge −**24, 25**
Beard, Lewis −3
Beaufort (S.C.) −10
Bellamy (Ala.) −27
Benjamin, Asher, Architect −3
Bennett's Mill Bridge (Ky.) −37
Benson Creek Bridge at Grafenburg (Ky.) −32
Big Bullskin Creek Bridge west of Shelbyville (Ky.) −32
Blakely (Ga.) −21
Blount County (Ky.) −2, 26
Boone's Knob Bridge (Ky.) −**31,** 32
Booth, Alf, and Rube Irvin, Bridge Builders −38
Boring Machine −6
Bourbon County (Ky.) −34, 35
Bower Brothers, Bridge Builders −36
Bower's Mill Bridge (N.C.) −6
Bowman, Col., of Elberton −31
Bracken County (Ky.) −36
Breckinridge County (Ky.) −34
Brice's Bridge (Tenn.) −28
Bridges, Covered. For a complete listing of existing covered bridges in the South, see Appendix II, pp. 46-48
Bridges, Covered, cost of, or value of −4, 6, 14, 24, 29
Bridges, Covered, Courting in −2, 20
Bridges, Covered, Designs and Plans −4, 10, **11,** 12, 32, **45**
Bridges, Covered, Disappearance of −1, 2, 15, 20, 25, 43
Bridges, Covered, Fortified −18, 40, 41
Bridges, Covered, Numbers of −5, 6, 9, 15, 20, 34, 37, 38, 42, 43, 46, 48
Bridges, Railroad, Covered Wooden −18
Bridges, Reason for Covering −54
Broad River Bridge near Carlton (Ga.) −20
Brush Creek Bridge −7
Bryant, W.T., Bridge Builder of Bellevue near Talbotton (Ga.) −17
Bunker Hill Bridge (N.C.) −**7,** 8
Burkeville (Ala.) −25
Burr, Theodore −11
Burr Truss Bridges −29, 33, **45**
Bush Creek (N.C.) −6
Butler Bridge (Ky.) −34
Buttahatchie River (Miss.) −38
Buttahatchie River Bridge −2, **39**
Buzzard's Roost Bridge (Ala.) −26 27

Calhoun County (Ala.) −26
Callaway Gardens −21
Camden (Ark.) −42
Camden (S.C.) −11
Camp Nelson Bridge (Ky.) −34
Cape Fear River (N.C.) −4, 5
Catawba River (N.C.) −5, 7
Cedar Hill (Tenn.) −30
Chaplin River Bridge (Ky.) −34
Chapman's Bridge in Gen. Pickens Division of Sumter Nat. Forest (S.C.) −14
Charleston (S.C.) −10, 11, 12
Chattahoochee River Bridge at Columbus (Ga.) −15
Chattahoochee River −16, 17, 20, 22

"Chattanooga Railroad Expedition" −18
Cheraw (S.C.) −10
Cherokee Lions Club −27
Chickamaunga Creek −19
Chickamauga Creek Bridge in White Co. (Ga.) −20
Claiborne County (Miss.) −38
Claremont (N.C.) −7, 8
Clarendon Bridge (Fayetteville, N.C.) −4
Clark's Creek Bridge −**40**
Clarksville (Tenn.) −29
Claysville Bridge (Ky.) −**33,** 34
Clintonville (Ky.) −34
Coheelee Creek Bridge (Ga.) −**21**
Colbert County (Ala.) −24, 26, 27
Coldwater Bridge (Ala.) −26
College Avenue Bridge, Athens (Ga.) −**20,** 21
Collin County (Texas) −43
Columbia (S.C.) −9, 11
Columbus (Ga.) −15, 17
Congaree River (S.C.) −9, 11
Congaree River Bridge −**9, 10**
Coosa County (Ala.) −26
Cox, John C. and T.A. −**6, 7**
Crooked Creek Bridge near Clarkson (Ala.) −26
Cullman County (Ala.) −26
Cynthiana (Ky.) −33

Daughters of The American Revolution −21
DeSoto River Bridge −**24**
Dix River Bridge (Ky.) −34
Doe River Bridge (Elizabethton,- Tenn.) −**frontis, 28**
Dover Bridge (Ky.) −36

Eagle Creek Bridge −**34**
Early County (Ga.) −21
Easley's Bridge (S.C.) −14
East Tennessee & Western North Carolina Railroad −30
Elizabethton (Tenn.) −28
Elkhorn Creek (Ky.) −34, 36
Etowah County −26
Etowah River −18
Euharlee Bridge (Ga.) −20

Fallsburg (Ky.) −37
Falmouth Bridge (Ky.) −34
Fayette County (Ky.) −36
Fayetteville (N.C.) −4
First Covered Bridge (N.C.) −3, 9
Flat Roof Bridge −**26**
Fleming County (Ky.) −36
Fletcher, Zouave Col. Thomas C. −41
Florida, Covered Bridges −38
Fort Gaines Bridge (Ga.) −17
Fox Creek (Ky.) −36
Frankford (Ky.) −32
Franklin (Tenn.) −30
Franklin County (Ky.) −36
French Bend River (N.C.) −5
Fuller, William A., Conductor who saved a Chickamaunga Creek Bridge and stopped Andrews Raid −19

General, Locomotive use in Andrews Raid, 1862 −18
Georgia, Covered Bridges −15
Georgia Historical Commission −21
Georgia, University of −20
Glass Bridge (Ga.) −**16**, 20
Goddard (Ky.) −36
Godwin, John, master of Horace King and Bridge Contractor (Ga.) −17
Gonzales (Texas) −43
Gonzales Inquirer −43
Granby (S.C.) −9
Graniteville (S.C.)−12
Grant, Gen. U.S. −42
Gregg, William −12
Greenup County (Ky.) −37
Goddard (Ky.) −36

Hall, Capt. Basil −11
Hamilton, Col. Wade −9, 11
Hardeman's Mill Bridge −1
Harpeth River Bridge −29, **30**
Haupt, Herman, Bridge Designer −7, 8
Hickory Level Creek −20
High Falls Bridge −5
Hillsboro (Ky.) −36
Honea Path Bridge (S.C.) −14
Horse Creek (S.C.) −12
Horseshoe Bend (Ala.) −**24**, 27
Horton's Mills Bridge (Ala.) −26
Howe,
    Iron and Wood Truss Bridges −17, 18, **19** 23, 28, 29, 34, **35**, 36, 42, 45 35, 36, 42, **45**
Hudson River (Ga.) −15

Ithiel (Town) Bridge (N.C.) −5

Jackson (Miss.) −40, 41
James Creek Bridge −38
Jamison, Robert, Bridge Builder −38
Jones, Capt. W.A.C., C.S.A. −26

Keener Steel Truss Bridge (Ala.) −26
Kentucky Covered Bridge Association −37
Kentucky, Covered Bridges −31
Kentucky River −31
Kentucky River Bridge −**32**
Keowee River (S.C.) −14
King, Horace, Black Freedman Bridge Builder (Ga. and S.C.) −17, 20, 22, 26.
King, William, John and Horace, sons of Horace −17, 20
Kirker, Isaac, Bridge Builder −36
Knox, Col. Samuel −12, 14
Knox's Bridge (S.C.) −**12, 13**
Knoxville (Tenn.) −28
Kymulga Bridge (Ala.) −26

Labor, Slave , Convict −6, 38, 43
Lafayette County (Miss.) −40
LaGrange (Ga.) −16
Landrum, Col. John J. defeated by Morgan −32
Lawrence County (Ky.) −37
Lee County (Ala.) −26
Lemy, Samuel, Contractor −5
Lewis County (Ky.) −37
Libby Prison (Richmond, Va.) −41
Licking River (Ky.) −32, 36
Licking River Bridge −**33**
Little Banks County (Ga.) −20
Little Beech Creek (Ky.) −34
Little Doe River Bridge at Hampton (Tenn.) −30
Little Pigeon Creek (Tenn.) −29
Little River (N.C.) −6
Little Uwharrie River (N.C.) −3
Locust Fork Bridges, Blount County (Ala.) −26
Long Bridge −**19**
Long, Col. Stephen H., Bridge Architect and Builder −37
    Long Truss Bridges −37, **45**
Long Crane Creek west of Troy (S.C.) −14
Longest Covered Bridge in USA −25
Louisiana, Covered Bridges −38
Louisville (Ky.) −37
Lower Gassaway Bridge (S.C.) −14
Lowndes County (Miss.) −38
Lownes, Moody CountyLine
Luxapalita Creek (Miss.) −38
Lyles Creek (N.C.) −7

Madison County (Ga.) −20
Margerum (Ala.) −24
Maryland, Covered Bridges (See Covered Bridges of the Middle Atlantic States)
Mason County (Ky.) −36
Maysville (Ga.) −20
Maysville Pike (Ky.) −31
McCallum's (Gen. Daniel) Railway Construction Corps −19
McCollom, Bridge Builder of Athens (Ga.) −20
McKinney (Texas) −43
McMillan, J.C., Bridge Builder −29
Meherrin River (N.C.) −5
Mellon Bridge (Ala.) −26
Mentone (Ala.) −24
Mills, William, Bridge Architect −10
Mississippi, Covered Bridges −38
Moffit (N.C.) −7
Monroe Count (Miss.) −38
Montgomery, Ala's Remington Bridge −23
Montgomery County (Ky.) −34
Mooney, John, Bridge Builder −43
Moore County (N.C.) −5
Morgan (Gen. John Hunt) Raiders −32, 33, 34
Myers Bridge (Ky.) −34

Nacoochie (Ga.) −1
Natchez (Miss.) −38
Natchez Trace Parkway −27
Natlee Bridge (Ky.) −34
Nelson County (Ky.) −34
Neuse River (N.C.) −5
Nicholasville Bridge (Ky.) −32
Noccalula Falls near Gadsden (Ala.) −26
North Carolina, Covered Bridges −3
North Middletown (Ky.) −34
Nunn, James, Bridge Contractor −20

Oconee River (Ga.) −17, 21
Oglethorpe County (Ga.) −20
Oldtown Bridge (Ky.) −37
Oostenaula River −18
Owen County (Ky.) −34

Paint Rock Creek (Tenn.) −29
Paris (Ky.) −33, 36
Paulding County (Ga.) −15
Peale, Charles Willson and Raphaelle −9, 10
Pearl River Bridgee, Prison −40, **41**
Pee Dee River (S.C.) −11, 12, 17
Pee Dee River Bridge at Cheraw −10
Phenix City or Girard (Ga.) −17, 22, 26

Pintlala Creek Bridge —**26**
Pisgah (N.C.) —6
Poole Mill Bridge over Sittingdown Creek (Ga.) —20
Port Gibson (Miss.) —40
Port Royal (Tenn.) —29
Prather's Bridge (S.C.-Ga.) —**14**
Pratt, Ex-slave Bridge Builder (Ga.) —18
Prison Bridge —**41**
Pumpkin Creek Bridge —**15**

Raleigh (N.C.) —5
Ramseur (N.C.) —6, 8
Ramsour, Andy L. —7, 8
Randolph County (N.C.) —4, 5, 6
Red River Bridge (Tenn.) —**29, jacket**
Reece City (or Reeceville) Bridge (Ala.) —26
Remington, John R., Bridge Builder (Ala.) —23
"Remington Bridge" design —23
Richland Creek Bridges —**4, 7**
Riddle's Mills Bridge (Ala.) —26
Ringgold Bridge (Tenn.) —29
Ringo's Mill Bridge (Ky.) —36
Robertson County (Ky.) —36
Robertson County (Tenn.) —30
Ruddle's Mill Bridge (Ky.) —**34**
Rutherford County (N.C.) —5

Salisbury (N.C.) —3, 5
San Marcos River Bridge —**43**
Sand Lick Creek (Ky.) —36
Sanders (Ky.) —34
Scruggs, Anderson M., Ga. poet —21
Sharpsville Bridge (Ky.) —34
Sherburne Bridges (Ky.) —34, **36, 37**
Sherman, Gen. William T. —4, 11, 17, **18,** 19, 42
Shortridge/Riffe Bridge (Ky.) —337

Skeen Mill Bridge (N.C.) —**3, 4, 6**
Smith, Ben, Bridge Builder of Dahlonega (Ga.) —17
Smith Truss —36
Sope's Creek Bridge near Smyrna (Ga.) —20
Sougchatchee Creek Bridge —26
South Carolina, Covered Bridges —9
South Licking Bridge at Cynthiana (Ky.) —3
Sowhatchee Creek Bridge (Ga.) —21
Spoon Bridge —**5**
Steens (Miss.) —38
Stone Mountain Memorial Park (Ga.) —20, 21
Stone, Stephen, Bridge Builder —34
Stoner Creek Bridge in Paris (Ky.) —32
Store-front portals —6, 7, 8, 43
Sucarnoochee River Bridge (Ala.) —26
Sulphur Fork Creek Bridge (Tenn.) —30
Switzer Bridge at Frankfort (Ky.) —34, **35**

Tallahatchee Creek Bridge (Ala.) —26
Tallapoosa River Bridges at Horseshoe Bend (Ala.) —**24,** 27
Tennessee, Covered Bridges —28
Texas, Covered Bridges —42
Texas, Locomotive used to stop Andrews Raid, 1862 —19
Thierman, John & Sue, Bridge Buffs —37
Toccoa (Ga.) —14
Tollesboro (Ky.) —37
Tombigbee River (Miss.) —38
Town, Ithiel —3, 5, 14
    Lattice Bridges —**3, 4, 5,** 7, **10,** 11, 13, 15, 18, 22, 23, 36, 38, **45**
Trinity River (Texas) —43
Truss types —4, 17, 29, 37, **45**

Tugaloo River —12, 12
Tumbling Shoals Bridge (S.C.) —14
Tuscaloosa Bridge (Ala.) —23
Two Bayou Bridge —**42**

Uwharries, mountains and rivers —5, 6

Vicksburg (Miss.) — 38, 41
Victoria (Texas) —43
Virginia, Covered Bridges (see Covered Bridges of the Middle Atlantic States)

Walcott Bridge (Ky.) —36
Warren, James, and Willoughby Theobald Monzani, British Bridge Architects, —12
Warren, Russell Bridge Engineer —12, 14
    Truss —**11,** 12
Warrior River Bridge —**22**
Washington County (Ky.) —34
Washington, George A., Bridge Builder —30
Wateree River (S.C.) —11
Waycross (Ga.) —19
Western & Atlantic Railroad —18
Westminster (S.C.) —14
West Point (Ga.) —19
Weston (Texas) —43
White Bridge —36
White County (Ga.) —20
Williams, Herman, Bridge Builder of Banks Co. (Ga.) —17
Winn, Joe, of Dadeville, Ala. —24
Wrenwag, Lewis, Bridge Builder and Architect —**31,** 32, 34

Yacona River (Miss.) —40
Yadkin River (N.C.) —3, 4, 5
Yatesville Bridge (Ky.) —37

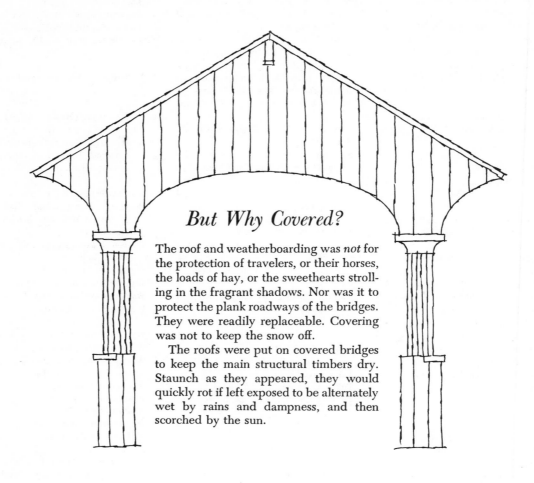

But Why Covered?

The roof and weatherboarding was *not* for the protection of travelers, or their horses, the loads of hay, or the sweethearts strolling in the fragrant shadows. Nor was it to protect the plank roadways of the bridges. They were readily replaceable. Covering was not to keep the snow off.

The roofs were put on covered bridges to keep the main structural timbers dry. Staunch as they appeared, they would quickly rot if left exposed to be alternately wet by rains and dampness, and then scorched by the sun.